Positive Beauty
A Practical Guide

Celia Hunter
with Charlotte and Denis Plimmer

Hutchinson

London Melbourne Sydney Auckland Johannesburg

Hutchinson & Co. (Publishers) Ltd
3 Fitzroy Square, London W1P 6JD

An imprint of the Hutchinson Publishing
Group

Hutchinson Group (Australia) Pty Ltd
30–32 Cremorne Street, Richmond South,
Victoria 3121
PO Box 151, Broadway, New South Wales
2007

Hutchinson Group (NZ) Ltd
32–34 View Road, PO Box 40–086,
Glenfield, Auckland 10

Hutchinson Group (SA) (Pty) Ltd
PO Box 337, Bergvlei 2012, South Africa

First published 1980
© Celia Hunter and Charlotte and Denis
Plimmer 1980
Illustrations © Hutchinson & Co. (Publishers)
Ltd 1980

Set in VIP Plantin

Set, printed and bound in Great Britain by
Fakenham Press Limited,
Fakenham, Norfolk

British Library Cataloguing in Publication
Data

Hunter, Celia
    Positive beauty.
    1. Beauty culture
    I. Title   II. Plimmer, Charlotte
    III. Plimmer, Denis
    646.7'2   TT957

ISBN 0 09 140751 6 212

To the pH factor
in my life

Contents

1 **The all-together woman**   7

2 **Mirror, mirror . . .**   12
What sort of person am I?   12
What is my overall impact?   13
Figure   13
Hair   15
Skin   16
Face   16
Hands   18
Feet   19
Clothes   19

3 **Your body: slimness, trimness, rest**   21
Fat isn't funny   21
The diplomacy of diet   22
Massage   24
Exercise   27
Sleep   35
The luxurious bath   36

4 **Your skin: what it does, what it needs**   37
Knowing your skin type   38
Allergies   40
Skin care   41
The treatment to suit your skin   43
Whiteheads, broken veins and cold sores   45
Oily skin   46
Dry skin   47
Combination skin   48
Suntan: the pros and cons   48
Massage with everything   49

5 **Make-up 1: basic principles**   53
Basic principles   56

Face-shapes: contouring, shading, blushing and highlighting   57

6 **Make-up 2: foundations and powder**   66
Foundations   66
Powder   72

7 **Make-up 3: eyes, brows and mouth**   75
Selecting and applying your shadow   77
A hint for a quick eye make-up   88
Eyebrows   89
Mascara   90
False lashes   91
Semi permanent false lashes   94
Party tricks   94
Spectacles and contact lenses   94
Eye care   95
Mouth make-up   96
Tooth care   98
Days of disaster   98

8 **Make-up 4: the essentials – cosmetics and tools**   100
At home   100
At work   102

9 **Hair: you and your hairdresser, home-care, problems**   103
You and your hairdresser   105
Doing your own hair   107
To tint or not to tint   111
Perms   113

Problems 114
Combs and brushes 115
'My hair looks ghastly' 115
Evening styles 116

10 Hands and feet: care and comfort 117
Hands 117
Feet 125

11 Excess hair and other nuisances 129
Excess hair 129
Personal hygiene 133

12 Fashion: the last word 135

Acknowledgements 141

1. The all-together woman

I have made up thousands of women. Many have been famous actresses. Many more have been models, for whom glamour is a way of life. You have seen their faces on posters in shop windows, advertising cosmetics. You have seen them on the covers of fashion magazines.

My work with these professional beauties has taught me a lot about my trade. But I have learned even more from the ordinary women whom I have also made up, the kind you see crowding along shopping streets, in and out of offices and factories, sitting patiently in launderettes. I have learned, too, from women with extraordinary problems, the physically handicapped, the psychologically disturbed and the blind.

Sometimes my 'canvasses' are faces and figures as near perfect as nature can make them. Far more often, I am challenged by the imperfections which bedevil us all: chins too small, noses or ears too large, busts too drooping, bottoms too broad, skins too coarse.

Because my hands are always touching faces, I can't seem to keep my eyes off them. I find myself staring at women as I ride home on the bus, analysing them, wishing that one would change the colour of her eye shadow, another, the way she wears her hair. And I keep asking myself, 'What is beauty?'

I can tell you what it is not. It is not necessarily the Venus de Milo's classic nose. Nor Diana Rigg's stunning figure. Nor Elizabeth Taylor's violet eyes. Glorious features are a bonus, of course.

But they are not the be-all of beauty.

I think the word should be re-defined. Beauty, I have found, is as much an internal as an external quality. You are drawn to people who are kindly, generous, pleasant, fun. A smile from a wrinkled face is more appealing than a cold, aloof stare from a smooth one. There is a sort of unity about people we admire. They are at peace with themselves, sure of themselves. They are composed. They hang together as personalities. They never seem to try too hard.

Beauty is being absolutely certain of who and what you are. Beauty is believing in yourself. You do not acquire these qualities merely for the asking. Certainly not for the dreaming.

Every time you enter a room, you make a statement about yourself. Before you say a single word, people have reached conclusions: 'She is lovely.' 'She is dowdy.' 'She is elegant.' 'She is vulgar.'

The most attractive women I have known have worked deliberately to become what they are, to control that vital first impact. This does not mean that they have spent either endless hours or vast amounts of money. It does mean that they have learned what is right for them. They have integrated themselves. They are *all-together* women. The hair style complements the make-up; the make-up suits the clothing; the clothing flatters the figure. What shows outside is an expression of what they are inside themselves.

This is not a case of striking the same note all the time. We all have a dozen different roles to play. Mood and manner and make-up are modulated, keyed at varying levels, as we shift from getting the kids to school, to making a pizza for the neighbours, to entertaining the husband's boss, to catching every eye as the great Glitter Queen at the ball.

In every circumstance, the goal is the same: to be an entity. To be sure of yourself in *that* role at *that* time. And to be seen by others to be so. In no case do you violate your personality. All personalities have many facets, and it's up to you to choose which facet the light is to strike at any given time.

I will always be haunted by a young woman I met at a party a few years ago. When I arrived, she was sitting quietly in a corner, and my eyes passed over her quickly. But they kept returning to her. I wondered why. Nothing about her was attention-getting. Her dress was unrelieved black. No fussy diamanté. No sequins. Her hair was dark, drawn back from her forehead, leaving her almost translucently made-up face a simple oval. This was a woman who flew no flags.

Her features were irregular, and you would have had to be generous to call her pretty. But her expression was cool, her eyes thoughtful and observant, with perhaps a hint of mockery in the calm gaze. Somehow she exuded a tremendous restrained sexiness. There were others in the room who far outshone her, and they were signalling to the men like mad. Yet within a few minutes, one man after another gravitated towards her, towards that quiet little gently-ticking time-bomb in the corner.

What was her secret? Self-confidence. She knew she looked as good as she possibly could. She had nothing to worry about. And she made all the over-triers and the razzler-dazzlers seem gauche by contrast.

The fascinating thing about her was that she could just as easily have been a little Miss Mouse. She could have shrugged and murmured self-pityingly, 'If God had meant me to be a beauty, he would have made me one.' But beauties aren't made in heaven – not entirely anyway. She was wise enough to know that. She had confronted her problems, and she had put them right.

I have never yet met a woman who, having learned to deal with one bad feature, has not gradually learned to deal with all the rest. Once you start, once you face the first challenge, then you move on step by step.

It's the women who give up without even trying who worry me, who decide that they are hopeless, and scurry into retreat without a fight. Too many of them overlook their assets, their good legs, shining hair or glowing skin, because they have let their faults intimidate them.

Some, with quite nice features, give up out of sheer lethargy. Here is one of the most exasperating cases I have ever run into. A few years ago, I was doing some before-and-after make-up demonstrations at a holiday resort. As usual, I asked for volunteers, and, as usual, many of the husbands pushed their wives forward.

One youngish woman kept resisting, even though her husband said he would take care of their two kids while I was making her up. He finally talked her into it. She was fairly pretty, but she was drab. She could have walked into the room and out again, and if I had been asked what she looked like, I couldn't have said anything definite. I guessed that she was about thirty-five. She turned out to be twenty-two!

I asked her what sort of make-up she usually wore.

'I don't normally do anything much. I can't be bothered.'

'At twenty-two, you've given up?'

'Well, I've got my husband and my kids. What else do I want?'

I was annoyed, and I spoke out frankly. 'How long do you think you'll keep your husband if you go on this way?' The expression on her face showed that this was something she had never even contemplated. I went on. 'There are a lot of girls around who are very attractive. He might be looking.' I paused to let that sink in, and then I said, 'You could be very attractive yourself. Come on. Let's prove it.'

Well, the make-up kit did its old magic. Half an hour later, she was younger, she was prettier and she seemed much more confident. When her husband came to pick her up, he said, 'You look fantastic!'

I didn't try to do a dramatic transformation job on her. That would have been a terrible mistake. She would have hated being suddenly turned into someone she didn't recognize. Her husband wouldn't have liked it much either. What I did do was to give her eyes more sparkle and her skin more glow. I also added some practical tips on how she could gradually transform herself.

A major tenet of the mysterious process of becoming beautiful is that it *is* gradual. It is never a matter of walking into a salon as Miss Mouse and walking out as Miss World. It is always a step-by-step evolution, so subtle that sometimes those closest to you don't even realize that it's happening.

Once you have decided that you want to do something – anything – about the impression you create, then you time a programme to suit your life. I believe in setting a goal and sticking with it. Let's say, 'I want a new Me by next Christmas' – or by my summer holiday – or by my birthday.

Keeping to your schedule isn't always easy. I know that. But you must give yourself no outs, make no excuses and stop whimpering. It's no good complaining that you don't have the time. I hear it again and again: 'I'm a working mother. I have to cook breakfast, rush to the office, rush back home and cook supper and then put the kids to bed. There's a basketful of ironing staring me in the face, and a dirty kitchen floor. Where am I going to find the time to sit back and fuss over my hair and hands and make-up?'

That's not an easy one to answer. A great many of us have to pack an incredible amount of activity into every twenty-four hours. There are few ladies of leisure in today's untranquil world. As I see it, it's a matter of making time for the things that really count. And how you affect those around you certainly deserves a pretty high priority. But you have to plan every hour, every minute.

I have worked out a couple of principles which my friends, with some amusement, call Celia's Laws.

The First: *Time is like an elastic band. There is always a bit more stretch in it than you think.*

The Second: *Never do only one thing, if you can do two at the same time.*

Let me give you an example of what I mean by planning. Today, let us say, is Monday. You have just received an invitation to a party for Saturday night. Six full days' notice. If you don't use time efficiently, you'll jot the date down in your diary and forget about it until – when? Maybe Saturday afternoon.

Now Saturday is a busy day in most households. If you're married, your husband is probably at home. You have to cook lunch as well as breakfast. If you're single, you still have all those niggly domestic jobs you always save for Saturday – your weekend shopping, your laundry. Saturday can turn into a rat-race.

But, wait. Today is only Monday. Surely you can spare twenty minutes today. Have a look now at the dress you plan to wear. Has the hem come loose? Tacking a few stitches when you're relaxed is easy; it can be a nightmare of knotted cotton if you do it in a last-minute frenzy. Does the dress need to be pressed? Does it need to be cleaned? (If you're in doubt about whether it is clean enough to wear, it is *not*.) Decide now and take it to the cleaner tomorrow.

Try it on first, though. A little too tight? Oh, damn! It's those four pounds you've gained. Not to worry. Between Monday and Saturday, anybody can lose four pounds.

Meantime, what about your gold evening shoes? Do they need heeling? Or are they beyond repair? If so, you have plenty of time to borrow from a friend, or to raid your mother's closet. Then check your make-up. Do you own the right shade of lipstick for the dress? And the right nail varnish? It doesn't matter if you don't. You can pick them up when you next go shopping. You are days ahead.

When Saturday comes round, wake up half an hour early to get your household tasks over and done with. While you are doing them, you are also doing things for yourself. Heat your hair rollers while you are making the beds. Let them work while you're writing your shopping list. Do your nails while the lunch is cooking. By evening, you will find that there is a beautiful empty gap for you to fill with a soothing sweet-smelling tepid bath.

Even now, you are still making the clock work for you, not against you. Brush your coat while your bath is filling. Let your face mask set while you soak. You are relaxed when you are putting your make-up on, and when you arrive at the party, you are ready to enjoy yourself.

Because what seemed to be a big problem last Monday has been broken down into a string of little problems. You have taken them calmly, one by one. You have outwitted time.

You can almost always make one minute do the work of two. But what about that other essential, money?

I often chat about beauty and make-up to groups of school girls, to women's clubs and to factory and office workers. I often hear the same complaint: 'I could look terrific too, if only I had the money.' There is a firm answer to that. Money does not buy what you want. It helps, of course. But you don't have to be rich to be well-groomed, to be an *all-together* woman.

Those beautiful cool ladies you see sauntering along Knightsbridge or Fifth Avenue or the Rue St Honoré, with their throwaway elegance, are not necessarily always the most expensively dressed. But they have that certain air I mentioned earlier, which makes you think they are. Let's look at one of them. You *assume* that the shirt she is wearing is real silk and that it cost a lot. Why? Because that's the sort of aura she creates.

If it *is* silk, it may be the only costly thing she is wearing. Even so, it might be three years old. A closer look might show that it's made of a miracle fibre, just like a lot of shirts you own yourself.

Let's concede, however, that she *has* spent money on some things. Maybe on her hair. Maybe on her shoes, or her handbag. But let's go behind the scenes and examine the rest of her outfit – the skirt, the jacket. They could just as well have come from one of the big chain stores (and very likely they have). It's not what she wears, but the way that she wears it.

It has taken a lot of planning to achieve that easy, casual manner. She has bothered to press her clothes the night before, and to assemble them and have them ready. She has thought about how she is going to fix her hair to suit what she will be wearing. She has chosen the right scarf, and made certain it is spotless.

These cool confident women don't just drag their clothes out of their wardrobes and shove them on at the last minute. They take the time to check in the mirror to see how they look from the back, to be sure that the skirt isn't creased, the hem down or the shoes worn at the heels. It is attention to detail that matters, and not spending money.

What goes for clothes goes for cosmetics too. It may give you an ego-boost to buy decorative jars with expensive names. And why not, if you can afford them? But if you can't, be thankful for the modern miracle that has placed on counters all over the world unguents and potions and lotions and fragrances that, in the old days, could have belonged only to the very rich.

Any woman today can, if she wants to, make the most of her potential. She has more going for her by far than ever Marie Antoinette had. The world is packed with goodies, all easily to hand, all designed to help us look our best.

And we have an obligation to do so. Or, rather, a series of obligations. The strongest of all is a selfish one – to you and you alone, who suddenly discovers a tingle of excitement in the joy of a new-found self-pride. But there are other obligations too. Tick them off: to the man in your life, who hates being seen with a slob; to your boss, who demands (and pays for) a well-groomed employee; to your kids, who go through agonies of embarrassment at having the frumpiest mum in the neighbourhood.

But – and here is an ardent plea – don't let your concern with Self become an obsession. This may seem a strange note to strike at the beginning of a book like mine, but we have all suffered from the 'beauty bore'. Who hasn't known the girl who is so all-engrossed in her own appearance that she has blotted out her personality, instead of enhancing it?

One of the dullest people I ever knew was one of the most beautiful and one of the glossiest. She was a fashion model, and it was her duty to be impeccable when she was at work. Her problem was that she could never let it rest.

I once went on holiday with her, and she spent almost the entire time either putting make-up on or taking it off, pressing her dresses or painting her toe-nails. She refused to walk in a breeze because it would rumple her hair. She was lacquered and brittle outside. And I soon discovered, as did the men who, at first glance, were bewitched by her, that she was brittle inside too. She was off-putting in every way. Although she was without a doubt the most dazzling woman wherever we went, she was also the greatest nuisance. She bored the other women. And she turned off the men. And I was never so happy as the day our holiday came to an end.

2. Mirror, mirror...

There is no way to tackle this whole business of making yourself look better except by facing the stark facts. The first step is a rendezvous with truth. You must ask yourself uncomfortable questions and give yourself honest answers.

Before we start, I'd like to make one thing clear. I don't much like people who are always telling others what to do. As far as I am concerned, this book is *not* a pulpit. I don't want to preach to you. But I do want to pass on a few useful ideas. Everything I propose derives from something I have worked out myself. And done myself. And helped others to do. So when I say, 'You should,' what I really mean is 'I've seen this work, and I'm pretty sure it will work for you.'

I am going to suggest that you do something utterly miserable – examine yourself feature by feature, inch by inch, analyse both your good points and your bad. As you go, you will reach some hard decisions and jot down your comments. Your notes will be a sort of written conscience. You are going to make a firm commitment to yourself.

Obviously then, before anything else, you will have to decide whether or not you are capable of doing that. So, ask yourself:

What sort of person am I?

Do I kid myself?
Do I keep my promises to myself?
Do I use my time sensibly, or fritter it away?

Do I forgive myself too easily, make excuses, find easy ways out?

If you can answer 'No' to all those, you're either the best woman around, or you're fibbing. Few of us can. You know whether you're sloppy or spasmodic or vague in your approach to life. You know if you're the type who goes on a week's mad crash diet, and then lets it all fall apart. You know if you have been promising yourself for weeks or months or years that 'some day' you would do something about your weight or your skin or your hair.

Well, 'some day' is here now. This is the moment to say, 'I know you, my girl. You've wriggled out of things so many times before. It isn't going to be the same again this time.' Or is it?

The sort of programme I have in mind isn't impossible for anyone. Not if you're able to come to terms with yourself. Let us assume that you are, and that you're ready to start on your intimate personal inventory.

There is only one way to find out what you look like. That is by studying yourself naked in the clearest possible light – daylight if practicable, otherwise, strip lights or lamps with their shades off. This is no time for soft flattering lights. They are liars.

You will need some paper, a pencil, a full-length mirror and a hand-mirror for rear and side views. If your notes are completely candid, you may want to lock them away afterwards. You might not even (or especially) want your husband or your best friend to see them.

Solutions come later. At this stage, you are only isolating problems.

What is my overall impact?

You are assessing the *all-together* impression that you make. Stand well back from the mirror and take your entire body in at a glance.

Ask yourself:

Are the various parts of me in proportion?
Do I look top-heavy?
Do I look spindly?
Is my natural stance graceful?
What is my type? Mum? Tart? Intellectual? Miserable old boot? Everybody's pal? Nobody's pal?
If the woman in the mirror were a stranger, would I envy her, or pity her, or decide she wasn't worth a second look?

My figure

Do I like my height? Am I too tall? Too short?

If you are five foot two, and wish you were five foot nine, there is literally nothing you can do about it. But you can create illusions with clothing and hairstyle that will make you look either shorter or taller. More important, you can adjust your weight to suit your height. A fat five foot two looks shorter than a slim one; a skinny five foot nine looks taller than a rounded one.

But think about it. What's so terrible about being either small or tall? Fashion pundits long ago decreed that the jargon word for short was 'petite'. Petite girls have desirable qualities. They are delicate (Dresden china figurines). They can seem vulnerable (so do kittens, and kittens do pretty well for themselves). As for tall girls, the words are 'queenly', 'stately', 'elegant'. At either extreme, your height can be a positive attribute.

Am I too fat? Too thin?

These are surprisingly subjective questions. All the charts that purport to tell

13

you what you *must* weigh for a given height and a given age are merely approximations. They can be widely off the mark. You are the *right* weight if you *look* right. The ideal is a well-covered body in good proportion – no fatty bulges, no ribs sticking out. For a woman of, say, five foot five, with narrow shoulders, the best weight is considerably less than for a woman of the same height whose shoulders are broad and whose bone structure in general is larger.

Only your own eyes can determine whether there is too much or too little of you. Almost every woman I know could easily afford to part with five pounds.

If you are one of the lucky few whose figure is pretty near perfect, please don't gloat. Today's body beautiful can become a disaster area tomorrow, *unless* you work to keep it that way. You may have to do as much to ensure that your lovely figure stays lovely as your less fortunate sister does to *make* hers so.

Overweight comes in three stages: plump, fat and obese. The last two definitely call for action, maybe even medical advice. But plump? Not necessarily. I can think of at least three successful and quite irresistible actresses who are what used to be called 'pleasingly plump'. The plump woman has a slight over-generosity where curves are concerned, but all her curves are in the right places.

If yours are too, don't fret, but do keep a watchful eye. The trouble with plumpness is that it can so easily slide one stage up the scale.

Am I flabby? Where? Stomach? Bottom? Breasts? Upper arms? Thighs? Back?

The dictionary defines the word 'flabby' as 'hanging loose by its own weight'. This is what I call 'the washing on the line look'. Flabbiness is an offence against yourself and against the beholder. You don't have to be either overweight or old to be flabby. Flab is the ally of neglect; it sneaks up on us all.

Look into your mirror – front, side and back – and note down any places where you are flabby. Toning up the muscles involved will come very high on the list of jobs you want to tackle.

Am I in proportion? Are my hips too large? Or too small? My waist? My breasts? Are my arms or legs too short? Too long?

Proportion is a matter of relationships, not girth. A big woman can be a handsome sight if her breasts, her waistline and her hips relate harmoniously, and all accord with her height and her shoulder-width. Here again, I put the charts that dictate 'ideal' measurements to one side. Of course, to be 34–26–34 is smashing. But inches on breasts, waist and hips can vary in either direction by a fair amount, and still add up to a pleasing figure, so long as there are no unsightly bulges in between.

Being a bit out of proportion can sometimes even be an asset. If your bottom is markedly too big, you will probably want to reduce it by exercise and massage. Be certain, however: you could be pummelling away an attractive attribute. (After all, women used to wear bustles to emphasize their derrières.)

What about your bosom? Most people want enough to establish a nicely rounded below-neck profile, enough, as the old French saying has it, 'to fill the hand of an honest man'. There is no such thing as an *exactly* right size or shape. What some of us consider overlarge or much too small is a delight to others.

Film stars have built entire careers on ample bosoms; models have done likewise on almost none. You can – but only within limits – enlarge, reduce or even reshape yours. More important (and far more practical) you can, with good posture and the right choice of clothes, make what you have look better than it is.

As for arms and legs, once more you are pretty well stuck with what God gave you. If your legs are too short (no one ever seems to worry about their being too long), there is not much you can do about it. The shape of both arms and legs, however, can be slightly improved by massage and exercise. Here again, optical illusion works magic. The clothes you choose, their colours, cut and length, can do for you what nature did not.

Do I have good posture? Do my shoulders slump? Do I hunch? Does my stomach or bottom protrude? Am I sway-backed? Do I stand pigeon-toed? Duck-footed?

It is amazing how an indifferent figure can be made to seem like a super figure if it is carried well. Shoulders back, stomach and bottom neatly tucked in, chin up – and you look like a woman who knows where she's going. What is more, you *appear* to have lost excess pounds; your clothes hang well and, with your head held high, you create an effect of self-assurance. You also feel better, because you have lifted your diaphragm so that you breathe better.

You never see a fashion model walking along with her head stretched in front of her like a bird's. Her chin is always slightly in the air. That's one reason why she stands out in a crowd.

Posture is important when you're standing still, when you're walking and when you're sitting. So check yourself in front of the mirror doing all three.

Congratulate yourself if you like what you see. Don't grieve if you do not. Of all the advantages a woman wants, good posture, that basic underpinning to everything else, is the easiest to achieve. With a little exercise and a little self-persuasion, it can easily and quickly become a routine, so much a part of you that you hardly have to think about it.

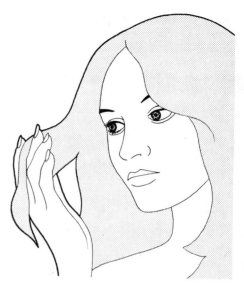

My hair

When you describe someone, how do you begin?

'She's short and blonde.'

'She's tall and dark.'

'She's a chubby little redhead.'

Hair and figure, taken together, before you are quite aware of a person's face – that's the combination you notice first. And what others see first in you.

Hair is to a woman what a flag is to a ship. It declares the colours she is sailing under. It can express mystery. It can say, 'I'm a tomboy', or an 'outdoor girl', or 'cool and self-sufficient', or 'wistful and waiflike'. It can also say, 'I'm an awful mess.'

Ask yourself, 'What does my hair say about me?'

Does it flatter my features? Complement the shape of my face? If I am short, does it make me look taller or squash me down like a mushroom?

Is it luxuriant? Thin? Lank? Naturally curly? Straight?

Is it the right colour for my complexion? Too harsh? Too mousy?

Is it well cut? Nicely shaped?

Does the style suit me? Or has it been forced on me by some 'expert' who convinced me that it was fashionable?
Is it dry? Oily? Normal?
Is it clean? Shining?
Are the ends split? Do I have dandruff? Is my scalp scaly? Does it itch? Is it sore?

Hair, to be beautiful, must be healthy. Severe scalp ailments and problems like split ends call for professional help. But most of what your hair demands can be worked out between you and your hairdresser, or even by you alone. And it doesn't have to cost the earth. Mostly it's a combination of good judgement and patient care.

My skin

Skin is what we have the most of. It covers every part of us, except our eyeballs, and it can differ widely from one part of the body to the next.

Starting with your face, and working down and around your body (don't overlook knuckles, elbows, feet, soles of feet – all danger points), these are the questions to ask:

Is my skin dry? Oily? Normal? Oily in some places, dry in others?
Is it rough? Smooth? Coarse? Chafed? Wrinkled?
Is it spotty? Blotched? Do I have blackheads? Whiteheads? Enlarged pores? Acne?
Am I pale? Sallow? Ruddy? Is my colour too high? Do broken veins show through?
Have I moles? Scars? Other blemishes?
Have I excess hair? On face? Arms? Legs? Body?

My face

Your face is two things. It is the shop-window of your personality. It is also an assortment of separate features (your mother's eyes, your father's chin, Aunt Sophie's nose), some of which may please you, some of which you may detest.

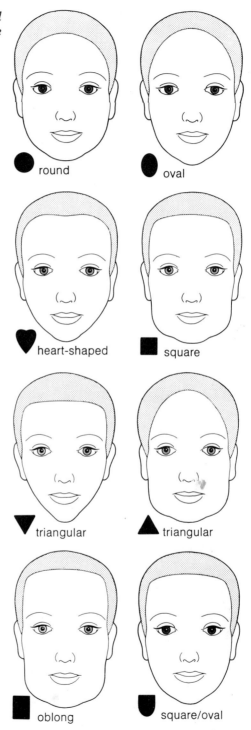

round

oval

heart-shaped

square

triangular

triangular

oblong

square/oval

16

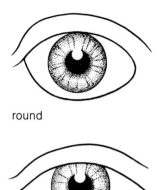

round

almond-shaped

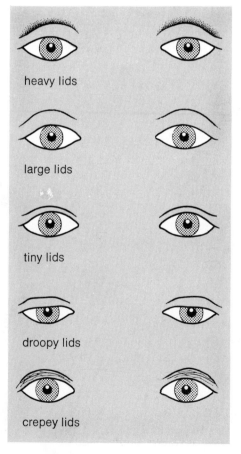

heavy lids

large lids

tiny lids

droopy lids

crepey lids

I don't think I have ever met anyone who is truly satisfied with her face. The important thing to remember (I know I have said this before and I will say it again many times before we come to the end of this book) is that there is far more to good looks than perfection of features. You can have your nose bobbed and your ears surgically pinned back; you can have the bags removed from under your eyes and the wrinkles in your neck tucked up, and still fall far short of your own ideal. And still be miserable.

Or you can come to terms with the face you have and be sought after, not *despite* it, but *because* of it. Can you imagine Barbra Streisand with a tailor-made snub nose?

One of my closest friends has an enormous mouth. She has very good teeth, but there seem to be far too many of them. Yet she doesn't go in for any silly nonsense about trying to make her mouth look small. She uses bright red lipstick and she smiles broadly. She has turned a disadvantage into an advantage, and she is a knockout.

You are – or can be – better-looking than you think. Study yourself front-face and profile while you answer these:

What is my face shape? (This is not an easy question to answer. Faces do not conform to a few simple standardized shapes. They come in a vast variety of combinations. So turn to the diagrams starting on page 16 before trying to answer.)

Is my face round? Oval? Heart-shaped? Square? Triangular? Oblong? A combination of several?
Are my eyes large? Small? Round? Almond-shaped? Protruding? Deep-set? Sunken? Too far apart? Too close together? (see diagrams, pages 79–88)
Are they bright? Lacklustre? Bloodshot?
Are the lids heavy? Large in area? Tiny in area? Droopy? Crêpey?
Do I have wrinkles under my eyes? Shadows? Bags?

*Are my lashes long? Short? Thick?
    Meagre? Straight? Curly? Dark? Pale?
Do my eyebrows grow too close together?
    Too far apart? Are they too heavy? Too
    sparse? Is their shape irregular? Attrac-
    tively arched?*

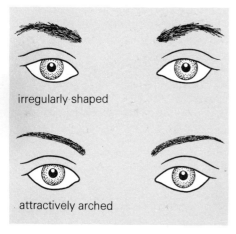

irregularly shaped

attractively arched

*Is my nose too large? Too small? Too long?
    Too short? Too broad? Too thin? Is it
    hooked? Bumpy? Are the nostrils too
    wide? Too pinched? Would I trade it in
    for a new one if I could?
Is my mouth large? Small? Prettily shaped?
    Lop-sided? Are my lips too thick? Too
    thin? Unevenly matched? Do the corners
    droop as though I were discontented?
    Or turn up, as though I were about to
    smile?
Are my teeth straight? Crooked? Broken or
    cracked? Do they protrude? Recede?
Is my neck too long? Too short? Scrawny?
    Wrinkled?
Do my ears stick out? Are the lobes too
    large?
How do I add up? Am I ugly? Passable?
    Pretty? Beautiful?*

Thank heavens for make-up! The art is
as old as the human race. Cleopatra
probably wouldn't have been half the
femme fatale she was if it hadn't been for
her little pots of kohl and other discreet
deceivers. Would the *grandes cocottes* of
France's royal court – the Du Barrys and
the Pompadours – have been quite as
devastating without their powder and
rouge and beauty patches?

We can only guess at the tricks
women got up to in the past. But we can
see for ourselves what miracles modern
make-up accomplishes. A make-up kit
can be to a woman what a palette is to an
artist – endlessly flexible, responsive to
challenge and infinitely subtle. It can
bring a good feature into prominence
and play down a bad one.

My hands

Poets have made us believe that the only
kind of hands worth having are long and
pale, with graceful tapering fingers. Very
nice, too – but not exactly common-
place. Nor even necessary, to be an
effective woman. How often, when we
see musicians' hands close up on tele-
vision, do they turn out to be strong,
broad, workmanlike? Spread yours out
and analyse them:

*Are my hands large? Small? Short and
    stubby? Long and lean? Strong and firm?
Is the shape attractive?*

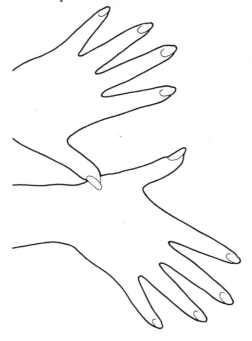

Are they dry? Chapped? Red?
Are my nails well kept? Are they clean?
*Are they brittle or tough? Too short? Too
    long?*
*Do I choose my nail varnish wisely? To suit
    my clothes? The occasion? My person-
    ality?*
Do I let my nail varnish chip or peel?
*Are my cuticles pushed back? Do I have
    hang-nails?*

Your hands are always doing something
that others notice. Because they are so
visible, they are an instant proclamation
both of your sense of fastidiousness and
of your personal style.

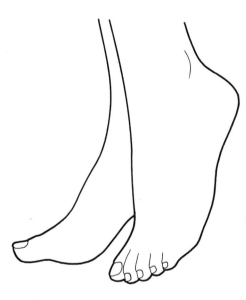

My feet

Feet are just the opposite. They are
seldom on public show, and consequently many of us treat them like poor
relations. We tend to tart them up only
in the summertime, when we wear
strappy sandals or go barefoot on the
beach.

But there are private viewings all year
round, and an ill-kept foot can kill
romance quicker than you think. It can
also do worse than that. Ignore it long
enough, and suddenly one day it will not
only look disgusting, but make you
wince with pain.

These are the questions to ask:

*Are my feet ugly? Reasonably presentable?
    Good to look at?*
Are my arches and insteps high?
Are my toes straight? Twisted? Gnarled?
*Is the skin smooth? Rough? All over? On
    heels? On soles?*
Do I have corns? Bunions? Callouses?
*Are the nails in good condition? Split?
    Broken? Well-shaped? Well-kept?*
Do my feet hurt? Where? Do I know why?
*Can I walk comfortably in high heels?
    Gracefully?*

Are your feet killing you? Or are you
killing your feet?

My clothes

We're almost at the end of your personal
check-list. But before we call it finished,
I'd like you to do one last thing. (If you
don't have time for this bit today, save it
for tomorrow, or the day after. But *do*
make time for it soon.)

Slip into your favourite outfit, the one
most people (women, as well as men) say
makes you look terrific. (I shall go into
detail about clothes in Chapter 12.)
However, since what you wear can never
be separated from the total illusion you
create, any changes you are contemplat-
ing in your face, figure or hair must take
your wardrobe into consideration. You
will be thinking about the way you dress
all through the programme you set yourself. For the moment, let's get a quick
impression:

Why does this outfit do so much for me?
What exactly does it do?
*Is it the cut that flatters? Or the length? Or
    the colour?*
*Does it camouflage my bad points (say, big
    hips)?*
*Does it draw attention to my good points
    (say, my bosom)?*

You will become more skilled at looking objectively at what you wear, as you get to know yourself – all of yourself – better. In the meantime, determining *why* this outfit is friendly and does you favours will help you to steer clear of all those other outfits which are your enemies and do you nothing but harm.

That really *does* finish your inventory. The notes you have made may look something like this:

Work out a realistic and relaxed schedule. If it becomes torture, your programme defeats itself. Don't prescribe a discipline so rigid that you will never be able to fulfil it.

You know how much time you can spare, from your job, your housework, your family. If you have only fifteen minutes a day that you can call your own, don't promise yourself more. You will be disappointed. But won't you feel pleased with yourself on the wonderful

Overall impact – Pretty good

Figure – Bosom-very O.K.
  Thighs- a bit heavy
  Tum - a little too much

Hair – A mess - Definitely needs
  rethinking
Skin – Sallow on face

etc.

What you have learned is what everyone discovers – that we all have faults. You have, probably for the first time in your life, isolated and admitted to your good points, your disaster areas, your possible trouble spots, and your unexploited advantages.

You have decided which problems you want to tackle most urgently, and which you can let wait a little while. Whatever they are – losing weight, toning muscles, putting new life into your skin – they all take time. Sometimes weeks, sometimes months. So don't set impossible targets.

day when you can stretch your usual fifteen minutes to twenty?

And don't expect miracles. You will not see dramatic transformations from one day to the next, not in your weight, nor in anything else. All these changes are gradual.

And one more 'don't'. Don't brood if you slip just a little. Your entire programme will not collapse if, say, one day you cheat on your diet. Your skin will not fall off your face if, say, one night you neglect to take off your make-up. If you let lapses like those become habitual, however, you could be right back where you started.

3. Your body: slimness, trimness, rest

Nothing made by the human hand, from a priceless Stradivarius violin to Concorde, is as exquisitely engineered as your body. Like a Strad or Concorde, it demands delicate tuning and constant care. Yet we take it for granted. We treat it shabbily. We abuse it. And we still expect it to go on working smoothly and efficiently.

The body, fortunately, is extremely tough. And extremely considerate: from time to time it sends out signals to warn us that something may be going wrong. Now, I have no intention of offering you medical advice. Distressing signals like persistent insomnia, recurrent headaches, mysterious swellings, sudden loss of weight and nagging pains call for a visit to the doctor.

Your doctor and I, however, are not so far apart. He is concerned with your health, and I with your beauty. The two go together. You cannot feel rotten and still look good.

So I shall urge you to heed the signals that usually warn of minor passing ills: an upset stomach, a sudden spot, circles under the eyes. I too shall 'prescribe' – that you try to maintain a sensible (and becoming) weight; that you do not over-eat; that you do not over-drink; that you tone and exercise your body; that you avoid becoming overtired. What I ask of you is common sense and an easy-does-it approach.

Fat isn't funny

'Everybody loves a fat man.' So the saying goes. Men, maybe. But women,
well, hardly ever. The ones who love them least are the over-heavy women themselves. It's not much fun to try to buy a dress and to be told, 'Sorry, but madam is really rather difficult to fit.' It's not much fun to know that people giggle cruelly when they watch you from the rear, with your bottom jiggling like blancmange.

More figures (to say nothing of romances) are ruined by overweight than by all the other problems combined. Only a few pounds extra can be unsightly. More than that, and the result is an awful mess.

Being too thin is far more rare, and it is often the direct result of some physical or psychological condition that will respond to medical help. Being fat is something else again. It *may* have a physical basis like a glandular disorder. Usually, however, it is caused directly by over-indulgence, either to compensate for private unhappiness or feelings of inadequacy, or, much more often, simply by making a pig of yourself.

Fatness has bred an entire vast industry: pills, health farms, saunas, low-calorie foods and drinks. Fortunes have been made by the inventors of fashionable diets. But tomorrow's régime may well contradict today's, just as today's has already contradicted yesterday's.

I myself am no great believer in sudden and dramatic weight losses. A sauna or a steam bath will indeed knock a couple of pounds off. But the loss is in body fluids, not in flesh, and it will come right back again. The chief advantage of treatments that make you perspire is that they cleanse your skin of impurities, and relax tense muscles. You can feel marvellous after you've had one. But don't kid yourself; you won't be thin.

As for crash diets, they should be resorted to only under extraordinary and temporary circumstances. It will do you no harm (as I suggested in Chapter 1) to cut down drastically on food for a few days, so that your favourite party dress won't bulge at the seams. But fad diets (eating only grapefruit or bananas or whatever is the current 'in' thing) carried on for any length of time can disturb your body violently, upsetting natural checks and balances. They may leave you exhausted and incapable of either work or play. They can make you look downright haggard.

In any case, they savour of rush and panic. It is gratifying, of course, to watch the arrow on your scale move down, rather than up. The sad fact is, though, that once you get down to the weight you want and abandon the diet, the arrow will swing rapidly into reverse.

A few exceptionally strong-minded women can use crash diets cleverly. They know that they need the stimulus of a quick sensational loss. Once they have seen results, they are cheered on. They can then settle into a consistent, commonsensical regime which not only brings their weight down, but *keeps* it there. I repeat: they are most exceptional.

The majority of us do better to start off at a slow and steady pace, and to maintain it. It is not too difficult to shed seven or eight or even a dozen pounds over a few months. The secret is to ease yourself gradually into new eating habits.

Some people claim that they can do it faster than that, losing on average two pounds a week. This is usually fairly easy at the start, especially if you are on the really roly-poly side. Weight loss is almost always most dramatic when you have large wads of fat to shed, and when your enthusiasm and strength of character are at their best. But it is not easy to keep losing at that rate regularly every week. Once you begin to backslide, you get discouraged and it is highly likely that you'll start gaining again.

This goes back to what I said in the first place about your entire beauty programme: set yourself a realistic goal that is not too demanding, and you will delight yourself. Set one that puts too much pressure on you, and you may chuck the whole thing in despair.

The diplomacy of diet

Dieting is nobody's business but your own. The fewer people you tell, the better. If you eat a little less or if you avoid certain fattening foods, without making a fuss, most of your family won't even notice. If you let this particular cat out of the bag, you will bring out the worst in everyone. At dinner, someone is sure to say, 'No potatoes for Janet. She's on a diet, you know.' Embarrassing and conversation-killing! Or some devil who is dying to see you fall from your tiny moral pedestal will deliberately tempt you: 'Come on, Jan, have another drink. Don't be a spoilsport.'

Secrecy is my preference. But you may be the type who flourishes on shared martyrdom. If so, a slimming club could do for you what you can't do for yourself. If you *can't* cut down without the example of other dieters, then, okay, that's your method. I have nothing against it. You may even learn a trick or two.

So long as you know what makes you put on weight, you can evolve a perfectly successful diet entirely on your own. Choosing what you eat, and what you don't, always gets back to controlling the number of calories you consume. This does not have to involve complicated mathematics. Count calories if you like, but it is not imperative.

We have all learned by now that cakes are more fattening than, say, oranges; that potatoes and rice and other starchy foods are bound to put more pounds on us than spinach or carrots or cabbage. We don't have to be told that large quantities of *anything* will leave more sticking to our ribs than small quantities of the same thing. And we all know that, to stay healthy, we need some protein foods like eggs, fish, cheese and meat.

There are dozens of painless ways to slash your intake. But don't expect your scale to applaud your efforts every single day. Results don't show up that regularly. It is next to impossible to lose at a steady *predictable* rate every twenty-four hours. Weigh yourself once a week instead of every day. The difference will show then, and you will experience a tremendous psychological lift.

Tailor your diet to your life-style. This is easier for the bachelor girl than for the married woman. If you live alone, nothing you do – or don't do – will disrupt anyone else's eating habits. But if you are a wife and mother, you could turn the entire household topsy-turvy. So be clever.

Cook the foods your family like. Why cheat them? You yourself need eat only part of the menu. Skip the roast potatoes and gravy; the others are not likely to notice. Or ring changes that will be good for them as well as you, and (if you don't say why) will even please them: fruit salad instead of pie; sorbet instead of ice cream; grilled fish instead of fried.

Every housewife has a lot of ready-made excuses for letting her diet lapse:

'I *had* to have scones and jam at tea. My mother was coming.'
'I *had* to bake a chocolate cake. It was Jim's birthday.'
'I *had* to make sausage rolls. The kids were giving a party.'

Of course, she had to serve them. But she did not have to eat them.

The career girl can fall back on a battery of similar excuses:

'I *had* to have three courses at lunch. Both my boss and his client had three.'
'I *had* to go to the cocktail party. I would have been a dead duck with my editor if I hadn't.'

Yet she is in a far better position to say 'No' than is the housewife. The waiter hands her a menu, and she makes her own choices. If you are that career girl, choose your three courses cagily. Avocado with shrimps is exactly eight times as fattening as clear soup. Steak and *béarnaise* sauce is about four times more fattening than grilled chicken, and profiteroles nearly five times as fattening as a chunk of Cheddar.

As for cocktail parties, they hold more traps for the unwary than there are holes in Emmenthaler cheese. It is not the drinks alone. It is all those sneaky nibbles and titbits. There are more calories by far in a handful of salted peanuts than in a large gin. I am not suggesting that it is better to be drunk than fat. But it is prudent to remember that you'll get fatter quicker on a dip made with mayonnaise than on a glass of champagne.

I have seen wonders worked by merely cutting quantities. Try 'halving' for a while. If you usually eat two rashers of bacon, eat only one. Take one slice of bread instead of your normal two. If you like milk and sugar in your tea or coffee, and drink six cups a day, drink three instead, and thus halve the fattening milk and sugar. (Even better, switch to artificial sweeteners and milk substitutes.)

You are going to slip. Of course you are. But you can atone today for your diet sins of yesterday. I often do it. And it works. There are times when you cannot avoid having a rich meal. This may indeed be because you *have* been dieting, and your body, literally starved of sweets and carbohydrates, is calling out

23

for them. A natural and normal reaction. Or maybe your hostess has gone to an immense amount of trouble, and you don't want to hurt her feelings by pecking at her prize dishes.

All right, then. Splurge – tonight. But tomorrow, eat nothing, or almost nothing, at all. No, it is not difficult. With the generous amount that you have consumed, you have stored up quite enough energy to see you through.

Some women stay slim because they are lucky. But most of those whose figures you admire stay that way because they have trained themselves never to let their weight get out of hand. The first signal – a pound or two up on the scale, or the slightest tightening of a skirt around the waist – and they put themselves on a semi-diet, either by paring a bit at every meal, or by skipping meals entirely.

There is nothing sacrosanct about three 'proper' meals a day. Nor does anyone have to eat by the clock. But when we are dieting, almost all of us find that at certain hours – usually the same hour every day – we are seized with an overwhelming craving. Perhaps trimming breakfast and lunch brings you no grief. Comes four o'clock, however, and you groan, 'I am famished!'

There are two things to do about that. The first is to remember your commitment to yourself. Harden your heart. Do something specific. Straighten out the files. Shorten your little girl's pinafore. Clean the silver. Anything to stop you feeling sorry for yourself.

The second alternative requires less strength of character. Simply fill the aching void with a non-fattening substitute. Drink plain soda and lemon juice with an artificial sweetener. Eat an apple or a raw carrot or a piece of low-calorie chocolate.

Too much weight can be mean and maddening. It is not only that there are too many pounds. It is that the excess can be so stubborn about the places where it piles up. The pear-shaped woman has a way of getting more and more pear-shaped – layer upon layer on thighs and hips. It is the same for the top-heavy woman; arms and bust are where she always adds more.

Just as maddeningly, when you begin to lose, the losses seem to come not where you want them, but where you don't. Your neck may start to look scrawny and your face a little gaunt before you can measure so much as half an inch off the too too solid flesh on the hips.

Discouraging? Not entirely. Not if you bear in mind that diet has a couple of stalwart helpers, and that these are massage and exercise. Not one of the three on its own will make you slim and keep you trim. Put them all together, however, and when you are on a losing streak, you win.

Massage

Massage to me is a kind of witchcraft. Used consistently, it seems to erase fat and flabby patches, to persuade them, almost to woo them, to go away. It does not actually remove pounds, but it breaks down fatty tissues and it tones up lax muscles, so you look thinner than you are, and far more svelte.

If your budget permits, it is a gorgeous idea to treat yourself to a professional massage once in a while. (Maybe someone will even make you a present of a course of them!) As I said, you won't come away any lighter. Only the hardworking masseuse loses weight. (At one period, when I was giving about seven or eight massages a day, I lost pounds and pounds.) The massage will relax you wonderfully. You will also pick up a few tips about how to move your own hands on your own flesh, so that you can massage yourself effectively at home. Even without a trip to a salon, you can master some simple techniques.

Since massage works best when you

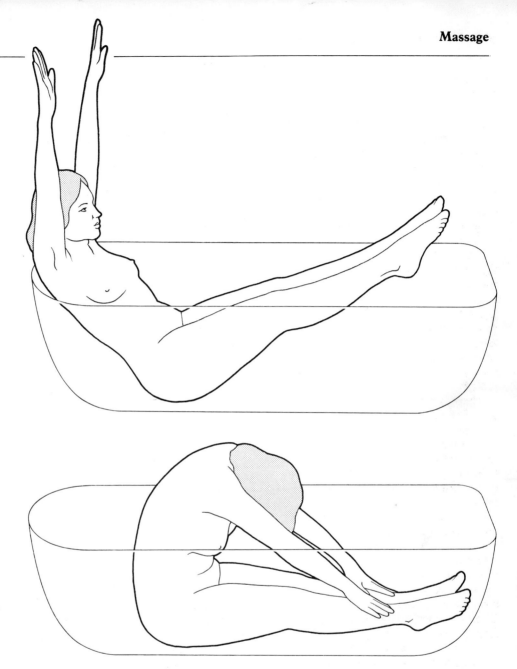

are warm and tension-free, the ideal place is in your bath. (Baths, of course, can serve you in a dozen other ways, and I shall talk about their sybaritic function in your life at the end of this chapter.)

First s-t-r-e-t-c-h your legs out full length, lifting them so they won't hit the end of the bath. At the same time, s-t-r-e-t-c-h your arms as high in the air

as you can reach. Stretch voluptuously the way a cat does. You should feel tautness all the way down to your toes and to your fingertips. Then relax completely. Now you feel a sense of muscular relief.

Bend forward from the waist, moving your hands as far down on your legs as you comfortably can – past your knees, towards your ankles, towards your toes.

I want to pause for a moment over that word 'comfortably'. *In massage, as in exercise when you come to it, you must never strain, never force your body to do more than it can. I cannot emphasize this strongly enough.*

Now you begin to work away at your particular trouble spots. Another word of warning: it is not wise to massage either your stomach or your breasts. The flesh here is sensitive and can be harmed. Any other part of you can take it, though.

Suppose you have a thigh problem. And a hip problem. Gently pick up a little wad of flesh in your fingertips, using a sort of plucking motion. I do mean gently. If you bruise easily, your own fingertips can leave you black and blue. (You can buy massage gloves covered with little nodules, which some women prefer to kneading with their fingers.) Pick the flesh up. Then let go. Do it again, and then again, gradually moving an inch or so at a time from place to place over your hips and around your thighs.

This movement can be doubly beneficial if you work on your left hip with your right hand, and vice versa. That way you are stretching your waist and your arms at the same time. Then move round and round one hip with both hands. Switch to the other side. You need do this only for a few minutes, but you should do it long enough to feel a tingling in your flesh and to make your skin blush slightly pink. Use the same plucking motion on the excess around your waist and on your upper arms.

Then soap yourself all over, again stretching as far as you can, across your shoulders and your back and down your legs to the soles of your feet. If you own a shower (even a hand attachment), turn it on full, both to flush the soap away and to let the spray massage your neck and back and shoulders, parts that you can't reach easily with your hands.

You continue your massage when you

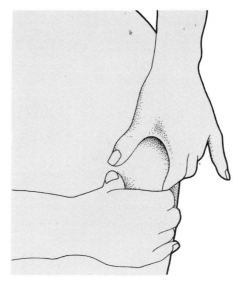

towel. Pull your towel briskly back and forth across your hips and shoulders, your thighs and bottom, turning from the waist. Then douse yourself with body lotion, and give yourself a final overall massage. This time, use a kneading motion. You compress the flesh between your fingers (held fairly closely together) and the heel of your hand. Working with both hands at the same time, move from the knee up the thigh,

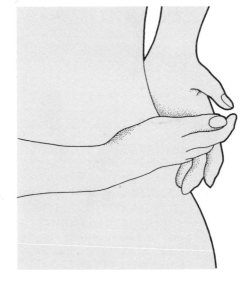

around the hips and around the waist. Then knead alternately with each hand on your upper arms. By now your skin is glowing. Your muscles are alive. And you are feeling astonishingly good.

You may not have time for all of this every time you bathe. But the results, I promise you, will begin to show after a very few days, even if you set aside only a few minutes each time.

Exercise

Exercise, like massage, will tone up your muscles and smooth you out. In conjunction with a sensible diet, it can also help you lose weight.

One of the best exercises of all is swimming, which puts practically all the muscles you possess to work. For those who don't enjoy ordinary exercise, dancing does the same – any dance, from ballet to rock. Just chuck yourself about for five minutes or so, in time to whatever music you like. I like music, in any case, when I exercise.

I am going to propose nine simple exercises which are easy, practical and require no equipment. In terms of time, they don't amount to much. I do them myself about five days out of every seven, averaging some seven minutes at a go. This adds up to slightly over half an hour a week. You need not do all nine at every session. But if you can manage it once in a while, then go through the lot, lingering over each one.

Some people prefer to exercise before they bathe, because the twists and turns make them perspire. But you really should take it easy and not work yourself into a lather. No rush. No panic. I prefer after the bath myself, when my muscles are already relaxed.

There are literally hundreds of exercises besides my nine, but I am fond of these because they all do double or even treble duty, helping the waist, the hips and the arms, for instance, at the same time. They are also good for posture.

It doesn't much matter what you wear, if anything. I have a sort of track suit, made of fine towelling. You might prefer a leotard or a bikini, so long as it is in no way restricting.

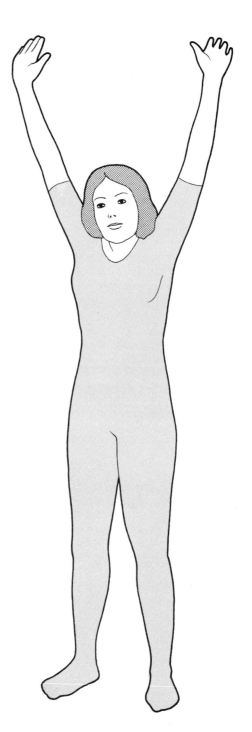

Here are my nine exercises. Do each as many times as you like. Twice or ten times. Slowly and gently. Take a half minute or so after each one, standing still, with your shoulders back, breathing deeply. Don't worry if at first you can't bend or twist as far as you like. You'll do them all more easily as time goes on, and your muscles become more supple.

1. Stand with your feet slightly apart. Slowly raise your arms and stretch upward. Push. Almost as if you were pushing the ceiling. Hold the position a few seconds. Then lower your arms. Try this two or three times. You should feel a pull on all the muscles above your waist.

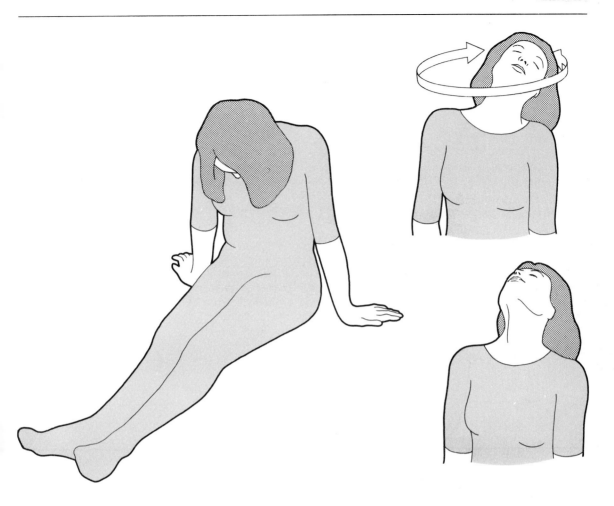

2.   Sit down, with your shoulders back and your head high. Let your head loll forward until your chin rests on or near your collar-bone. Then, very slowly, rotate your head from left to right or from right to left, whichever you prefer. It is a circular motion. Now roll your head backwards as far as you can, until you feel the flesh under your chin grow taut. Roll your head round and forward again.

Then left. Right. Back. This relaxes the muscles in your neck and at the top of the back. It also helps fight double chins. You can do it almost anywhere, especially when you feel a crick in your neck. You might get an odd glance or two in the typing pool, but pay no attention. You'll probably find before long that the others are copying you.

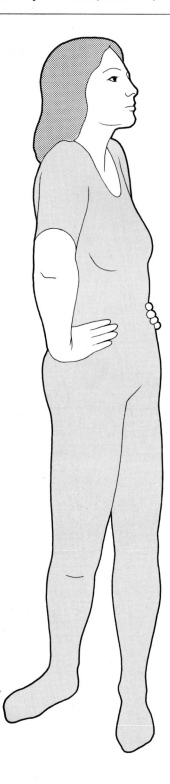

3. Standing, place your hands on your
hips and slowly twist the upper half of
your body to the left. Then to the right.
Your hips should remain motionless.
Twist from the waist up only.

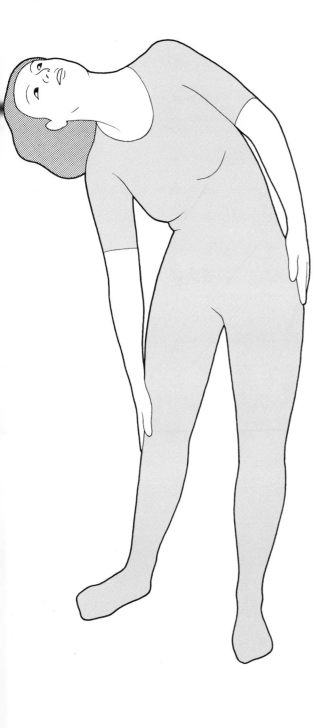

4. Stand with your feet slightly apart and your arms dropped. Let your hands relax with the palms resting against the outsides of your thighs. Slowly bend the upper part of your body sideways, first to the left, so that your left hand slides gradually down the left thigh. Straighten up. Then bend to the right, sliding your right hand down the right thigh. Straighten up.

5. Stand with your feet slightly apart and your arms dangling loosely. Keeping your knees straight, bend forward slowly, reaching as far down as you can. *Don't try to touch your toes unless you can do so easily.* But with every bend you will find that you reach down a little bit further.

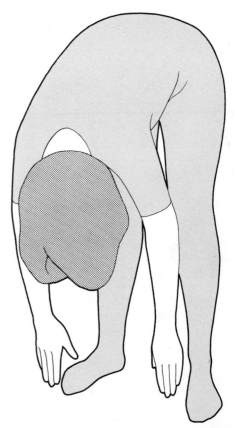

6.   With your arms outstretched to the sides, rise on your toes and balance on the balls of your feet. Slowly, keeping your back straight, lower yourself into a squatting position. Still on the balls of your feet, hold the position for a moment or two. Rise, but still without resting your heels on the floor. Once again, down to squatting position. And rise. You will feel a pull in the muscles of your legs, your thighs, your shoulders and your stomach. As soon as the strain becomes uncomfortable, stop. Two or three squats should be enough at first.

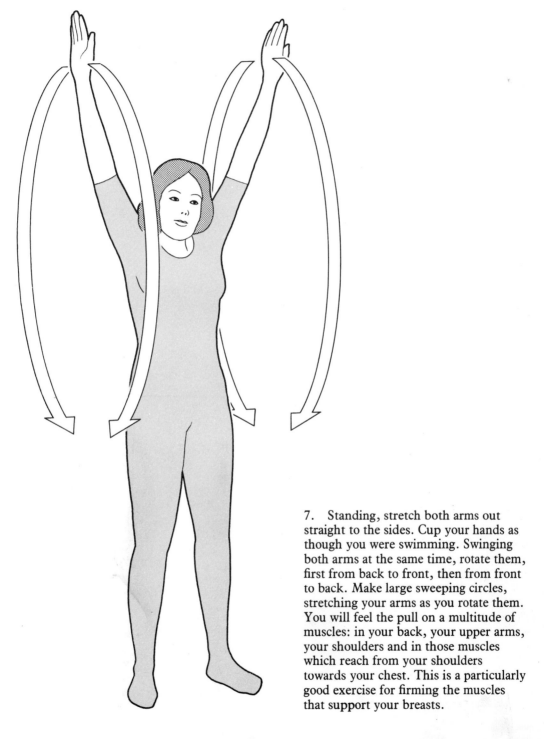

7.   Standing, stretch both arms out straight to the sides. Cup your hands as though you were swimming. Swinging both arms at the same time, rotate them, first from back to front, then from front to back. Make large sweeping circles, stretching your arms as you rotate them. You will feel the pull on a multitude of muscles: in your back, your upper arms, your shoulders and in those muscles which reach from your shoulders towards your chest. This is a particularly good exercise for firming the muscles that support your breasts.

8.   Lie flat on your back with your arms stretched alongside you. Do this on the floor, not on a bed, because the mattress will not provide enough resistance. (This holds true for any exercise you do lying down.) Gradually raise yourself to a sitting position, using the muscles of your midriff to pull you up. Do not help yourself by using your hands. At first you may not be able to raise yourself all the way. If you cannot, lie back, relax, breathe deeply and try again. After a few days, your muscles should have strengthened enough for you to do this fairly easily.

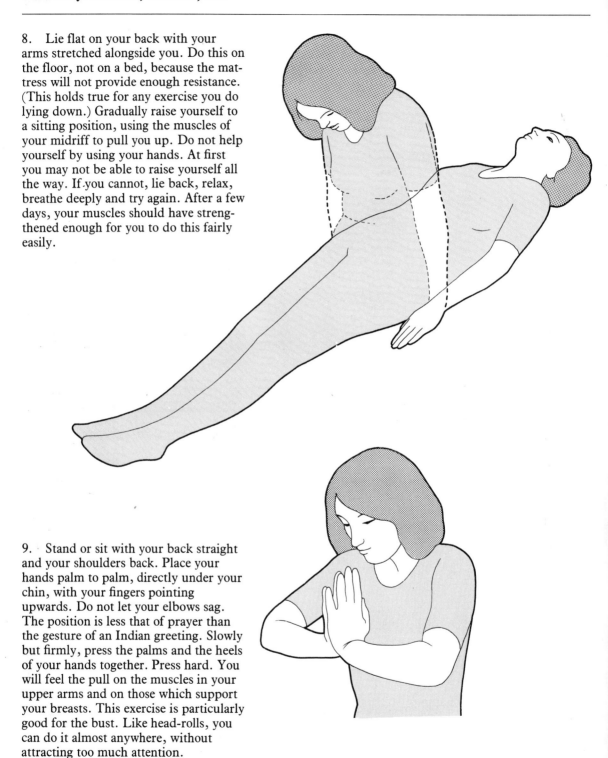

9.   Stand or sit with your back straight and your shoulders back. Place your hands palm to palm, directly under your chin, with your fingers pointing upwards. Do not let your elbows sag. The position is less that of prayer than the gesture of an Indian greeting. Slowly but firmly, press the palms and the heels of your hands together. Press hard. You will feel the pull on the muscles in your upper arms and on those which support your breasts. This exercise is particularly good for the bust. Like head-rolls, you can do it almost anywhere, without attracting too much attention.

If you ever catch yourself thinking, 'Oh, lord, now I have to do my exercises again,' you are on the wrong track. They should not be a burden. They should be a pleasure.

In any case, almost all of the movements in the all-purpose set that I have given here are movements that you normally make in the course of any ordinary day. Think of the easy ways you can work all those useful twists and stretches into your regular routine.

Hold your arms up straight and push towards the ceiling when you're reaching for a jar on a high kitchen shelf. Give your arms and legs a good stretch when you bend to put on your shoes. Move your upper torso, keeping your hips still, while you are sweeping the floor. Squat with your back straight when you dust the bottom rung of a chair.

Think up some for yourself. A little ingenuity is all it takes. Each of the exercises you work into your routine need last no more than a second or so. All those seconds added together will definitely make a difference in your body's muscle tone.

Sleep

Shakespeare called sleep the 'chief nourisher in life's feast'. We don't all, however, need eight full hours every night. A lot of us get along perfectly happily on no more than seven, or even six. Different bodies dictate different terms. And it does seem rather a pity to invest one-third of one's entire life in keeping the other two-thirds going, if it isn't really necessary.

But the sleep we do get should be sound. There are a number of ways to prevent tossing and turning. Be sure that your bed is comfortable. A bumpy, lumpy, squashy mattress can murder sleep. There is no uniform 'comfort formula'. What works for others may not feel right for you. So experiment. In general, though, you are likely to welcome fairly firm support and to sleep better (and fight a double chin at the same time) on one pillow instead of two, in a room that is coolish and a bed that is warm.

But what if you have worked out the ideal circumstances, and you are still restless? Ask yourself why. Have I gone to bed in a temper? Did I eat too much too late? Was I so excited over something wonderful (or something horrible) that I couldn't turn off my mind?

If sleeplessness is a recurrent nuisance (not grave enough to call for a visit to the doctor, but bothersome a couple of nights a week), then be good to yourself. Make yourself a cup of herbal tea or a warm milky drink. Soothe yourself with dreamy fragrances. Buy a pillow filled with hops or herbs. Spray the room with your favourite cologne. Rub a minute drop of an essential oil from which good perfume is made – say, jasmine or verbena – into the crook of your arm. (I myself am partial to neroli, the essence of bitter oranges.) The fragrance is pervasive, and it will gradually calm you. It will also help you to think pleasant thoughts.

Pleasant thoughts, hopeful thoughts, happy thoughts – all are sleep inducers. It is hellish (and don't we all know it?) when you can concentrate on nothing but your problems. Now, I am not so naïve or stupid as to tell you to forget your worries. If you face a serious dilemma, you can't just wish it away. What you can do, however, is to think about it practically. Make one positive decision. Decide that tomorrow you will discuss what is on your mind with your bank manager, or your husband, or your doctor, or your son's headmaster – that you will at least make a start on reaching a solution.

Often, though, we fret ourselves into sleeplessness over nonsensical things: the colour of a new dress; why we said 'yes' to an evening out with someone we don't really fancy; why the cake didn't rise.

Think how silly you are, and laugh yourself out of these.

Under the best of circumstances, you cannot force yourself to sleep. You shouldn't be exhausted, but you must be ready. It is a mistake to say, 'I have to get up at five tomorrow morning to catch a train, so I'll go to bed at eight.' You can't kid your body into thinking it is time to rest three hours before it is accustomed to doing so. Better to go to sleep at your regular hour and snooze on the train tomorrow. (A snooze is a lovely thing, in any case, whenever you can manage it. For heaven's sake, don't feel guilty if you steal a quarter of an hour for a nap on a busy day. You'll be far more efficient afterwards.)

One last word. The worst way to court sleep is to pursue her. She will only elude you. If you cannot sleep, don't struggle. Give up, get up and do something useful. Mend a dress. Turn out a cupboard. Write a letter. And before you know it – zzzzzzzzzzzzzzzzzzzzz.

The bath luxurious as switch-off: a once-in-a-while treat

It will be no secret to you by now that I am an advocate of self-indulgence. As far as I am concerned, nothing makes me feel more pampered than a long, luxurious, sweet-smelling bath. Nor more relaxed.

Whenever you can steal the time, afternoon or evening, whenever you can have the bathroom all to yourself with no fear of anybody banging on the door, then settle down to a soothing, voluptuous soak. Choose whatever product does your skin the most good (see Chapter 4) and, for a change, just *bath*. Don't worry about exercises or massage. Simply be nice to yourself.

Buy yourself a bath pillow to put under your head, above the water level. Or do what my mother, who adores the fragrance of herbs, has done. She has punched tiny holes in a polythene bag and used it to cover a herb pillow. When she lies in her bubbles, the steam releases the aroma, and it wafts about her like incense.

Take it nice and easy. Read a book (preferably, for your library's sake, a paperback). Have a gin and tonic. And if the phone rings, ignore it. If it's important, he will call back. (It will probably be a wrong number anyway.)

4. Your skin: what it does, what it needs

Skin is the most incomparable packaging material in the world – adjustable, self-fitting, self-renewing and protective. If it could be retailed in handy rolls, no home would be without it.

It acts as a non-stop thermostat, helping us to maintain a comfortable temperature. In cold weather it makes us shiver, and shivering actually helps to warm us. The cold also makes the tiny hairs all over the body stand up (you never see this, but they do) and this traps the air and creates a warming layer of insulation.

In hot weather the skin perspires. Perspiration evaporates. Evaporation is a cooling process. Hot or cold, the skin always sweats a bit, and that flushes the body of impurities. But that's not all.

Skin is an early-warning system. Because the nerve-endings are just beneath the surface, the skin is the first to know when anything is going wrong. It will say to you, 'Hey, you've cut your finger.' Or, 'You're getting a blister on your toe.' Or, 'You're standing too close to the heat.'

Skin is immensely appreciative. It adores being stroked, cuddled, cleansed, massaged. It is politely grateful when you brush beach sand or snowflakes off it. It goes quietly mad over silk or cashmere. Marvellous, isn't it?

But it can get cross. Because there is so much of it, it can be troublesome in a lot of places and in a maddening number of different ways. It will go blotchy, itchy, patchy, scaly. It will break out in rashes and erupt in spots. Listen to all its messages and it will serve you well. Ignore them at your peril.

Skin is always changing, and a keen watcher will notice minute differences from one morning to the next. Sometimes the signals are as dramatic as a fire alarm: an angry rash, a bright red bump, a sudden dry patch. Most problems, however, arise more gradually, and we become aware of them only after several days, or even a week. Usually these are reactions to things we have done wrong, and usually, if we think about it, we can trace the trouble back to its cause – to lackadaisical care, perhaps, or to something we have eaten. Too much citrus fruit can make a dry skin even dryer. Too much chocolate can make an oily skin come out in spots. (Allergies are a burden on their own, and I shall talk about them separately.)

Sometimes the warning signals are at first invisible, and our fingers can tell us what our eyes will not. So it is essential to feel, to touch. Your fingers will register a bump that is beginning beneath the surface. They will serve notice that your legs are getting bristly, that your elbows are rough.

Skin is not just skin-deep. What you see is merely the outer or top layer of the epidermis. Beneath that, there are a half dozen layers more. The top layer is constantly dying and being sloughed off, and the layers beneath pushing up to take its place. (You get a completely new skin about once a month.) Under the

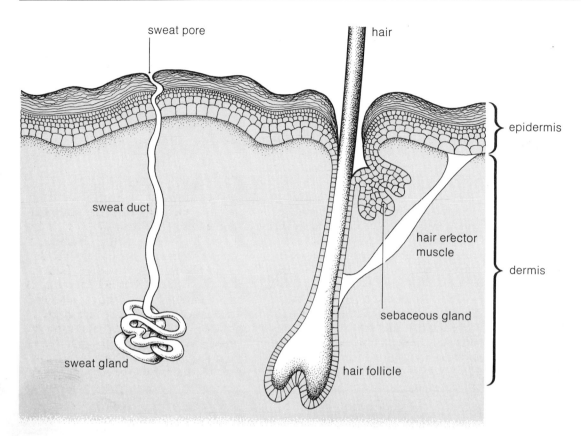

epidermis there is still more skin, another thicker layer, the dermis, in which the sweat glands, the oil glands (called the sebaceous glands) and the hair follicles are rooted. The dermis, too, keeps pushing upwards to provide new epidermal layers which will in turn reach the surface, become dead skin cells and flake off.

It is vital to make certain that those dead skin cells are effectively removed, briskly rubbed away. If they are not, they clog the pores. They keep the skin from breathing. They make it look dingy and unsightly. When they are permitted to pile up in places that undergo constant pressure, like the heels and soles of your feet, they become hard and calloused and painful.

We take it for granted that skin must be kept clean. Outwardly clean, that is.

But it needs cleansing from the inside, too. This involves drinking plenty of water to help the skin do its job of flushing away impurities. How much is plenty? There is an old saying that we all need eight glasses a day. Maybe so, maybe not. Eight glasses seems a lot to me, since we take in liquid in many ways – from other beverages, from fruits and vegetables, from soups and so on. But we can all do with several glasses in addition. I sometimes take mine warm, with a slice of lemon in it, especially in the morning.

Knowing your skin type

A completely normal skin is as rare as snowballs in July. By 'normal' I mean neither too dry nor too oily. I mean supple and pliant and clear. If we are lucky enough to be normal on parts of our faces or bodies, the chances are that other parts have gone awry. Almost all of us have combination skins: oily in some places, dry or normal in others.

There is no great mystery about determining which type is yours. If it is dry, it feels tight. It tends to flake and scale, to chap and wrinkle easily. If it is oily, it feels far more relaxed. But it is likely to have enlarged pores and to be prone to spots and blackheads. Oily skin looks – what else? – oily. The make-up you put on before you leave home in the morning can begin to streak and shine by the time you reach the office. Touch your face with a piece of cleansing tissue, or with your fingertips, and you will see an oily residue.

With a combination skin (let's think for the moment about the face where the mixture is likely to be most extreme), the oiliness will probably occur in the centre panel. You will see signs of it from the middle of your brow, down the nose (especially around the nostrils) and in the little hollow between your lower lip and your chin. If you wear your hair in a fringe over your forehead, blackheads are likely to breed underneath.

The rest of your face, however, can be normal, or (how exasperating can nature get?) it may even be over-dry. The same holds true for the body. An oily back and shoulders can belong to the same unhappy woman who has dry legs and arms. As though things weren't complicated enough, there are also seasonal changes. Dry skin gets even dryer when it's either too hot or too cold. Oiliness gets oilier in the summer, especially indoors. However, sunshine in moderate doses can do oily skin a power of good. I'll go into this in more detail when I discuss the pros and cons of suntan (see p. 48).

Models moan and groan to me a lot about their skins, far oftener about their being over-oily than over-dry. This is understandable. When you are young, oiliness creates many more problems, more sludge-clogged pores, for example. But it has its compensations for the future. As one ages, the sebaceous glands become less active, and an oily skin turns normal. In addition, with all those decades of natural lubrication, it is likely to remain smoother longer than a dry skin, to retain more easily the elasticity of youth and to stave off wrinkles for a few extra years.

None of us can avoid wrinkles, but they are not necessarily ugly, nor even displeasing. One of my favourite wrinkle stories comes from Queen Elizabeth, the Queen Mother. For her sixtieth birthday the famous photographer, Cecil Beaton, took the official photograph that was to be released to the press. When he brought her the proofs, he suggested tactfully that he retouch the one she chose, ever so slightly, just to brush a few wrinkles away. 'Please don't,' she said. 'I would not want it to be thought that I have lived for sixty years without having anything to show for it.'

Showing lines of character is one thing. Looking wizened like a dried old prune is something else again. This need not happen. You do something to your skin 365 days out of every year. Do it badly – dragging, pulling, using products that can harm – and every single day of those 365 you encourage wrinkles to set in. Do it well – nourishing your skin with the correct products for its type, supporting and firming the muscles beneath – and you hold wrinkles at bay.

You have probably heard that you should never frown, and that you must not let the corners of your mouth droop. That's fine, if you have nothing to do in life but to concentrate every second on your expression. But most of us are not quite that preoccupied with self, nor quite that artificial. Our faces show what we feel – anger, sorrow, happiness, mirth. How dull we should look if they didn't! All we can do is try to counteract the traces of these emotions that autograph our skins. The earlier we start, the better.

Wise mothers teach their daughters to do this as soon as they begin to use make-up. But, you say, *your* mother was not that foresighted. And here you are, at thirty or so, with little crows' feet already lightly etched at the corners of your eyes and laugh lines beginning to show. Can you get rid of them? I hate to say it, but it isn't very likely. At least, not entirely. You can make them look less sharp, iron them out a little by massage (see Massage, p. 49) and by stimulating, toning and feeding.

Before we get down to skin-care, let us pause to consider those miserable and often mystifying manifestations known as allergies, as they affect the skin.

Allergies

Allergies may show up as spots or rashes or red blotches. They can parch your skin or make it swell. They can result from something you have eaten; something you have worn; something you have applied to your skin; a dog or cat you have patted; dust or pollution in the very air you breathe.

There was even a case not long ago of a bride who turned out to be allergic to her husband, although it is hard to understand why she didn't find out before she reached the altar.

An allergy is usually – though not always – caused by some element that is new to your routine. Change your make-up, your perfume, your soap or your diet, and you could come out in spots, perhaps immediately, perhaps after several days. When this happens, you are seldom baffled. You ask yourself, 'What unfamiliar substance have I introduced?' You need not be a Sherlock Holmes to work it out. You remember, and you simply give it up. You also know if, over the years, your skin has

reacted badly to, say, wool or nylon. Experience has taught you to pass those fabrics by.

Allergies often give subtle warnings as they begin to creep up. You may become *aware* of your skin in a way that you usually are not, aware that something strange is going on, perhaps a mysterious feeling of tightness or a slight stinging sensation.

Allergies are most disconcerting when they give you no clue as to their cause. You may be able to tolerate just so much, but not a millim more, of a given fragrance in a given range of cosmetics. (You don't know this, of course; only your skin does.) You have used the same brand regularly for months, or even years, and then suddenly one day you begin to itch. That is because you have pushed the limits of your tolerance that fraction too far.

But how can you possibly know that *that* was what went wrong?

Stress and tension, or merely growing older, can cause certain things to bother you (food as well as cosmetics) which have never bothered you before. Milk, for instance, or strawberries – lovely one day; poison the next.

Again, how do you discover the cause?

When it comes to questions of this kind, which you cannot answer for yourself, you need the help of your family doctor or of a dermatologist.

There are quite a lot of things that many of us find hard to take:

1. Anything that is sprayed on with an aerosol shoots forcefully into the skin like tiny arrows. This alone can irritate, if you are sensitive. So can the chemicals in the spray. (Should you react badly to aerosol products, you could just as easily be irritated by furniture polish or window cleaner as by cosmetics used directly on your skin.)

2. Perfumes, especially those with a chemical rather than a natural base. (One answer: wear them on your hair or

on your clothes, not on your skin. I always do myself.)

3. Deodorants. These require careful experimentation. Many are far too harsh.

4. Frosted eyeshadows or lipsticks. The ingredient that makes them iridescent can also irritate. (You can often discover this in advance by trying a bit on the back of your hand or on your inner arm. If there is the slightest burning sensation or the faintest flush of redness, they are not for you.)

5. Nail polish. This is less apt to affect the hands themselves than the face. A difficult one to isolate, because it isn't likely to occur to you that touching your skin with polished nails might irritate.

6. Suntan products. Despite their value in blocking out harmful rays, many contain fragrances which can affect certain skins adversely. The fact that they are always worn in intense heat may accentuate the harmful reaction. A consolation: non-perfumed products are available.

There is a kind of blotchiness that fits almost, but not quite, into the category of allergies, and which springs up unexpectedly on your neck, at the top of your bosom or on your arms. It can come from bad circulation. More often it arises because you are nervous or upset. It is as uncontrollable as blushing, and far more embarrassing. Its sense of timing is atrocious – when you have a crucial job interview, or when you're trying very hard to impress a tableful of dinner guests.

Hot baths can sometimes make blotching worse; tepid is better. And alcohol can bring it on, all on its own; so don't try to soothe your nerves with a pre-party drink. If blotching is your problem, you can't easily solve it, but you can conceal it. Low necklines are dead giveaways; high necklines tell no tales. You can still have your allure, still show

a bit of flesh, with a slit from the neck down (if you dare) to the navel. No one but you is aware of what you are hiding underneath.

Skin care

Your skin will never look attractive, no matter how cleverly you make it up, unless it is in good condition. You cannot paint successfully over a rough and dirty wall. The same holds true for a rough and dirty skin.

I first became skin-conscious at a very early age, eleven, in fact. I didn't start to use make-up that young, of course, but I did start taking care of my skin. Perhaps this was because my mother's skin has always been extremely sensitive, and mine is like hers. There was nothing precocious about this childhood start; it was no more abnormal than regular childhood visits to the dentist.

One fundamental skin-care routine applies to all types of skin. All must be cleansed, toned, moisturized. The products used, however, will vary from one type to the next. I shall go into some detail later about what sort each type demands. In the meantime, here is a list of essentials which we all should have:

1. A loofah or a long-handled bath brush to rub away dead skin cells on the body and to stimulate. A strip of old towelling will work as well. Fold a length – about two feet – into three layers, and then sew strong loops of tape at each end, to serve as handles. (A complexion brush – optional, and only for oily-to-normal skins – does the same for your face.)

2. A pumice stone, to do the same for heels, soles, and elbows (see Chapter 10).

3. Bath oils, milks or bubbles. Or your favourite herbs (camomile, for instance) tucked into tiny bags which you make of muslin and hang under the hot tap so that the water pours through.

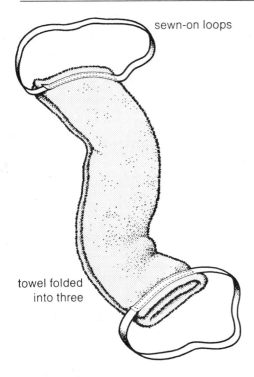

sewn-on loops

towel folded
into three

4. Body lotion.

5. Body powder.

6. Face cleanser (cream or liquid).

7. Face toner.

8. Face moisturizer.

9. Face mask.

Don't let this list terrify you. The individual items need not be costly. Buy the famous, expensive names if you can afford to and, as I said in Chapter 1, if they give your ego a boost. But no product has to put you in hock to be efficient. (I will remind you of this again when we reach the section on make-up.)

The basic ingredients in beauty products vary only minutely from the most expensive on the market to the least. The difference in cost to you depends upon a number of things, some of which are for your benefit and some of which are not. Don't be fooled. High prices may buy higher-quality fragrances. But they also subsidize ritzy packaging, fancy jars and bottles and heavy advertising, none of which does your skin a scrap of good.

I myself (and a lot of other women I know) bypass some commercial products entirely for certain skin-care procedures. I rub my elbows with a cut lemon to remove the dinginess. Instead of a cleansing cream or lotion, I use liquid paraffin. It is pure and clear. It may not suit you; you could find it slightly sticky. But if you do like it, you won't have had to sell the family silver to pay for it. It costs only pennies.

I use a mixture of rosewater and witch hazel as a skin toner. I vary the formula slightly from season to season. In the summer, I mix it half and half. In the winter, when I want a less astringent effect, I mix it, four parts rosewater to one part witch hazel.

As for bath unguents, you can get away with a drop or two of almost any soothing oil – almond, rosemary, olive, oils made for babies. There is a certain domestic danger, however, in all oils. You must scrub the bath thoroughly (great exercise for you) when you are through. If you don't, you risk the life and limb of the person who follows you in.

Face masks, too, can be do-it-yourself. For oily skin, try the beaten white of an egg. For spotty skin, fuller's earth may do the trick; either follow the instructions on the packet or mix one tablespoon with half a carton of yoghurt. For dry skin, combine the yolk of an egg with a few drops of almond oil. For normal skin, you can use a nourishing, soothing mixture of yoghurt and honey: one tablespoon of honey to half a small carton of yoghurt (and eat the other half with honey). In a salon where I once worked we used to give favourite clients a luscious mask of strawberries and cream mashed into a purée. The strawberries were stimulating, and the cream, nourishing. Non-dieters were also served a bowl of strawberries and cream to eat.

Naturally, I'm not going to suggest that you grind your own talc for bath powder. But you can save a lot of money and be nice to your skin at the same time by buying powders made for babies. These have two advantages: they are extremely gentle, and are therefore unlikely to distress dry or sensitive skins; and they contain no strong fragrances which might fight with the perfume you put on later.

After-bath powder is especially comforting on hot days, because it helps to absorb perspiration and to combat chafing. Watch how you go, though, if you are planning to wear dark clothes. What you have patted under your arms and on your body can easily be transferred to your dress as you pull it over your head.

The treatment to suit your skin

Cosmetics manufacturers are, for the most part, reliable. Of course there are a few con-artists around who make unfulfillable promises about how their 'magic mystery' ingredients will transform you overnight. And they will charge you unconscionably for your gullibility. But all the big established companies spend millions on research. They concoct products specifically designed to do specific jobs. They tell you no lies when they label one for use on oily skin, and another on dry. So you can feel pretty safe when you buy. It is up to you to choose the one which suits your skin and your purse.

It is downright silly not to be careful about your choice. It stands to reason that a preparation evolved to counteract oiliness cannot help but be too drying for a skin already crying out for oil. And the reverse. Determine what you must have, and don't let anyone bamboozle you into taking anything else.

Many of us suffer from an imbalance between alkalinity and acidity. Acidity helps to fight off infections and resist certain allergies. Not enough acidity, and your skin can go spotty; too much, and it can go dry. The alkalinity counteracts the effects of over-acidity, just as bicarbonate of soda counteracts too much acid in the stomach. The correct balance is about fifty-fifty. If your balance is wrong it can show up not only in spots or dry patches, but in extremely strange ways. Does your make-up sometimes baffle you by changing its colour when it's on your face? If so, it could be because you have too much or too little of one or the other.

The alkalinity-acidity relationship is known as the pH factor. There are numerous products on the market – cleansers, toners and so on – marked 'pH balanced'. If you need them, they are a good investment. If not, why bother?

Don't become an addict of any product. If you use the same thing year after year, your skin gets bored and blasé. So do you. Surprise it and yourself with a new variety of the right formula. You get the pleasure of playing with something different, and your skin wakes up appreciatively.

Never let a day pass without at least one deep-down clean-up job on your face. Night is the logical time, obviously, because that is when it is the dirtiest. (You also always cleanse completely whenever you re-do your make-up afresh, as for an evening date, and not just a touch-up.) Use your cleanser generously, but not all in one go. *Half* the amount used *twice* is more effective than a great glob only once. Smooth it on gently (following the movements described in detail in the Massage section on p. 49), and remove it with a tissue or cotton wool dampened slightly in water and squeezed almost dry. Get every last smidgin of make-up off. Then tone and moisturize. The moisturizer

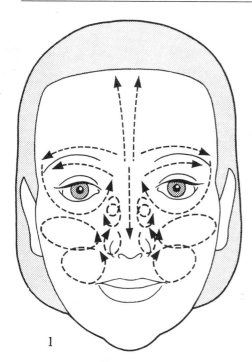

1

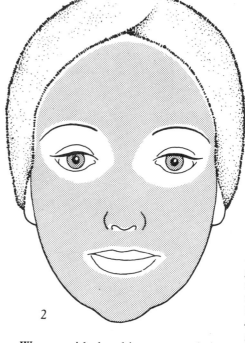

2

1. Composite picture of all massage movements, shown step by step on pages 49–52. These are the movements which should also be used when applying or removing make-up, cleanser etc.

2. Face mask. See below and page 45 paragraph 1

not only lubricates your skin, but – more important – it helps it to retain its own natural moisture.

If your skin is very dry, finish up with a dollop of nourishment before you go to bed. But *not* every night. Some nourishing creams are exceedingly heavy and may drag and pull in delicate areas, such as under the eyes. Some are greasy, as well, and can be most off-putting to your bed-mate.

Under no circumstances should we ever be rough with our faces. People with oily skins often make the mistake of treating them too vigorously. And people with dry skins, not quite vigorously enough.

I have known women with oily skins to scrub away mercilessly with harsh soap and to follow up with even harsher toners. And what does the skin do? It reacts logically. It says, 'Oh, my God, I'm getting dry!' So it sets the sebaceous glands to working overtime, and creates even more oil than there was in the first place.

Women with dry skins express their fears in the opposite way. Timidly, they reject anything which they suspect might be even slightly drying. They believe that they must constantly lather themselves with moisturizers. This too is a mistake, unless the skin has first been properly prepared – that is, unless all the dead cells have been removed. If they are not, the moisturizer will merely trap them, and create unsightly bumps. So a dry skin, as much as an oily one, requires the regular use of skin tonics. It can also do with a treatment once a month or so with a gritty cleanser, a cream or lotion which contains minute abrasive granules, designed to rub away the pile-up of dead cells.

Now to the face mask. This is a valuable periodic treatment to combat dinginess and spottiness, to speed up circulation, to stimulate and to tone. I suggested earlier some concoctions you might make for yourself. If you use a commercial mask, be absolutely certain it is the right one for you.

Some are moisturizing, some are drying, some are bracing. Some must be washed off, some can be removed with a tissue, there are some that peel away. Whichever you choose, follow the directions carefully. Tie a scarf around your head, so you don't get the stuff in your hair. Never spread the mask close to your eyes or on your lips. Do not leave it on longer than the instructions specify. You can have too much even of the best of things.

If you use a stimulating, drying, tightening mask, once a week is quite often enough. If it's a nourishing mask, twice a week. If you can't manage time more often, then settle for once a month.

One more thing: you are not at your most glamorous when your face is plastered with gunk. This is the moment for privacy. Shut the door firmly against the man in your life. He is your audience, after all. Don't let him peep behind the scenes.

Whiteheads, broken veins and cold sores

No one skin-type more than any other is *consistently* prone to these three evils. All flesh is – or can be.

Whiteheads, like blackheads, are unsightly little bumps. Because they remain under the epidermis, however, they do not darken. There are two varieties, one of which, again like blackheads, is caused by concentrated accretions of oil; the second type are hardened deposits of calcium. The former are likely to occur with oily or combination skin, the latter with dry. It is important to ascertain which type of whitehead yours are before you try to tackle them.

Hard, acidy whiteheads may result from a diet that is too heavy on dairy foods, which creates a calcium build-up. Cutting down on milk and cheese may get rid of them. Eventually, as the layers of skin flake off, whiteheads work their way to the surface and many of the cal-

cium type will then respond to masks. Do make certain that you buy a mask especially designed for the problem. When the oily type reach the surface, they may, with care, be treated like blackheads (see page 46), but there is no guarantee of success.

Whiteheads of either type are persistent little devils. It is possible – and I say this with big red warning signals – to have them removed by electrolysis. The operator must be absolutely expert. In careless hands, the electrolysis needle can leave permanent scars.

Broken veins appear most often on fine sensitive skin, but others suffer them too. The face is more likely to be marked than the body. However, as we grow older – say, after thirty-five or so – they sometimes appear on thighs. They are caused by a sudden gush of blood into the minute, thread-thin ends of veins.

Something as serious as high blood pressure or as trivial as blowing your nose too hard can be responsible. Too many tipples over too many years will almost always leave a tracing of broken veins. So, unfortunately, will too many emotional crises. Try to avoid circumstances which raise your blood pressure. Don't use strong face masks or astringents.

Broken veins, also, can be removed by electrolysis, but the same warning goes: *only* by an expert. Even then, I'm not sure that it is worth either the expense or the discomfort. If you have a tendency towards them, they are likely to return, and you're right back where you started. They can be covered quite effectively (see Foundations, Chapter 6), which seems to me to be the wisest solution.

Cold sores, despite their name, don't necessarily tie up with having a cold. They are, as far as anyone knows, caused by a virus. They can be quiescent for months, or even years, and then suddenly erupt when you are nervous or tense or getting ready for an important occasion, or when you've been exposed to too much sun.

Only medical treatment will help. You can (see Foundations) disguise them ever so slightly with a medicated foundation, applied with extreme delicacy. But if they were mine, I think I would leave them uncovered until the medical treatment specified had done its job.

Oily skin

You want to declare war not only on the oiliness itself, but also on the unpleasant byproducts it nurtures. The most conspicuous are that exasperating team, blackheads and enlarged pores. Blackheads are caused by an accumulation of your own natural oil, plus dirt, plus old make-up. Together, they form miniscule plugs which enlarge the pores. Each pore has its own set of muscles, and the plug stretches them. It is possible, with fastidious care, to reverse the process – after you are rid of the blackheads.

How to get rid of them? That is the question. If yours is a very serious problem, that is, if there are quite a number and they seem deeply and stubbornly embedded, I would strongly urge you to have them removed professionally. This is money well spent. The operator knows exactly how to go about it. She will be efficient, and once having worked with *your* skin, she will advise you both on prevention and on future treatment. (A peppering of blackheads on your back and shoulders, quite definitely calls for a pair of hands other than your own to banish them.)

If the blackhead problem on your face is not severe, you can deal with it quite safely on your own. *With caution.* First cleanse your skin scrupulously. Make absolutely certain that you have removed every last vestige of grease.

Then prepare a clean face-cloth. By clean, I mean hygienically clean: boiled. Apply it to your face as hot as you can comfortably bear it. But don't be a

masochist. No hotter than you can *comfortably* stand. Repeat this three or four times to open your pores as completely as possible. (A good time for this treatment is after a warm bath, because your pores will have already been urged to open; and last thing at night, because your skin should rest afterwards.)

Now – and here is where you must be extremely cautious – cover your index fingers with clean tissues and gently ease the blackheads out. Never, never use your fingernails. Never, never try to force the plugs. You are *easing*, not *squeezing*. If the blackheads won't budge readily, then give up and try again in a couple of days. Once they have popped out, go quickly over your face with a tonic or freshener, to cool the skin and help close the pores. After that, cover every spot you have touched with a mild antiseptic solution or an antiseptic cream. *Apply no make-up immediately afterwards.* That is why I suggest bedtime. Make-up could start an infection or a new pile-up of grease in those now distended and slightly sensitive pores.

For a few days afterwards, repeat the hot face-cloth treatment, followed by your cooling tonic. Ideally, you should continue this once a week, indefinitely. The muscles of enlarged pores will gradually be encouraged to work again.

Far better to avoid getting blackheads in the first place. You must always be careful to remove your make-up completely. Use a cleanser especially designed for oily skins. There are some which you cream on in the normal way, but which you wash off with water. These are better for you and cleanse more deeply than soap and water. Ordinary soap can be too drying, even for an oily skin. You can use a medicated soap, however, but no more than a couple of times a week. Once a week, use one of those gritty cleansers I mentioned earlier; not only do they rub away dead cells, but they also remove surplus grease.

In whatever way you have cleansed, you have massaged your face several times, both in applying the cleanser and in removing it. The skin, therefore, is warm and the pores are wide open and eager to soak up any oil that might possibly enter from your make-up. So close them. Close them tightly with that same cooling tonic.

Now you are ready for your moisturizer. Yes, you do need a moisturizer, but you must choose one which is not too rich. Employ it, depending on how bad the condition, usually no more often than every other day and only under the eyes and on the sides of your face where the oiliness is less extreme.

The last thing you want to do is to over-nourish your skin, so forget about night creams. Your ordinary moisturizer, applied at bedtime, will feed your face quite enough. You may not even need it all over, especially when you're young. As you grow older and your sebaceous glands get lazier, a little extra nourishment may be in order. But not usually before thirty or so.

Dry skin

Dry skin lacks oil or moisture, and more often both. You must drink plenty of water to put extra moisture into your thirsty skin, and try to avoid extremes of heat and cold which take the moisture out.

You are fighting a tendency to flake, to chap, to crack, to wrinkle. Your skin needs constant lubrication. It is up to you to give it externally the oils your body does not produce in sufficient quantities. Fortunately, dry skin laps up oily products gratefully, and reacts in a comforting way.

Massage a rich cleanser gently into your skin, and remove it with care. Follow with a toning lotion. You may have deluded yourself into believing that a toner will only intensify the dryness. Not true. You select yours carefully, of course. But, as I said before, you do need one – to remove the dead cells, to stimulate your skin and to prepare it to accept the moisturizer that will follow. This you apply lingeringly, warming it with your fingertips until it is completely absorbed.

Never use soap and water on your face, unless you are prepared to indulge yourself in one of the extremely expensive soaps recently introduced by certain fancy-name cosmetics manufacturers. As for your body, take care to choose a soap (there are many which are not costly) made especially for dry skin.

In some ways, you are lucky. You can slosh body lotion all over you. You can treat yourself often to soothing, moisturizing face masks. You can indulge in opulent, decadent creamy baths. In bathing, again you must choose your product with discrimination. Bath salts are often far too harsh for you. Some bubble baths are made of detergents; you can almost feel them tightening your skin. You wouldn't wash your dishes without rubber gloves. So why soak yourself in something that's too strong for your hands?

If you suspect that yours contains detergent, be your own scientist. Any chemist shop will sell you litmus paper. Put a drop of bubble bath on to a piece, and if it turns blue-ish or lavender, it is alkaline, and hence detergent. Even so, all is not lost. Tip a drop or two of oil into your bath, or a big splash of body lotion. The bubbles will be less buoyant, of course. They will also be more kind to you.

You have an overwhelming urge to nourish your face. But no matter how dry your skin, don't overdo it. You will eventually need a night cream, but you don't want to start too early. Usually not before thirty, and not more than once a week. If you overtreat when you are young, what on earth can you give your skin when it begins to scream for attention in your forties?

Combination skin

You are in good company. The majority of us are a mixture, dry or normal in some parts, oily in others. A combination skin really must be treated as two different types. If you try to compromise by using the same products all over, you can seriously harm one section.

But you don't have to go dotty about this. Favour whichever part of you needs the most active help. Ask yourself, 'What is the worst bit? Is it very dry? Very oily? Sometimes? Always?'

Let us say that you suffer from the most usual complaint, oiliness down the centre panel of your face, and either dry or normal skin to either side. You can quite safely use a normal-to-oily cleanser all over. But here is where the special 'two-faced' care comes in: you will use toners and moisturizers designed for oily skin in the centre. On the sides, you will use those made for dry or normal.

This is not a terribly difficult routine to follow. You may have to buy two bottles (or jars) to begin with, but it doesn't cost any more in the long run, because they will last you twice as long.

You can, with your tonic, buy what is best for the troublesome centre panel, and use it neat there. For the two sides, dilute it with several drops of water (this is easiest on a piece of cotton wool) to diminish the powerful drying effect. No sacrilege: water is a basic ingredient of all these products.

Obviously, if dryness is your greater problem, then you favour the dry sections.

Suntan: the pros and cons

I once met a lady on an expensive Mediterranean beach who lay all day long in the sun and sighed happily, 'Oh, how I love it. I feel like a lizard.' That summer she looked pretty marvellous. She had the most super tan in the place. She glowed warmly and softly, an amber goddess. Well, I met that same lady about five years later on the same beach.

And she was still at it. But now, she not only felt like a lizard. She looked like one. Her face was cross-hatched with deep, sharp wrinkles. She was certainly a champion at knowing how to wreck her skin.

Suntanning to extremes is a northern, twentieth-century vice. It began in the 1920s, as part of a publicity campaign to entice tourists in the summertime to the beaches of southern France. (Before that, the Côte d'Azur was fashionable only in the winter.) Those who were attracted came mostly from cold northern countries. And most of them had pale sensitive skins.

Until then, tanned skin had been regarded as a social abomination. Ladies protected their creamy complexions with dainty parasols, and they were right to do so.

A little sunshine is good for us all. A touch of bronzing can be flattering. Taken in sensible measures and very, very gently, exposure to the sun brings direct and obvious benefits. Oily skins can recover from spots. Dry skins, if they are well lubricated, can relax, ease up a bit. But proper protection is imperative. As well as the suntan aerosols, creams and lotions that we all know, there are various protective foundations and lipsticks (see Make-up, Chapters 6 and 7) which are especially formulated to screen out the harmful ultra-violet rays and to encourage gradual tanning without burning.

One menace persists, however, in the best of circumstances. Whenever we spend any length of time in the glaring sun, we all screw up our faces. Wearing sunglasses helps, but it doesn't entirely prevent this. Every grimace we make is an invitation to a wrinkle. These show up particularly at the corners of the eyes.

We would not stand in front of a fire and deliberately sizzle ourselves, even to the point of blistering. So why do we condemn our skins to agony on a beach or on a ski slope?

48

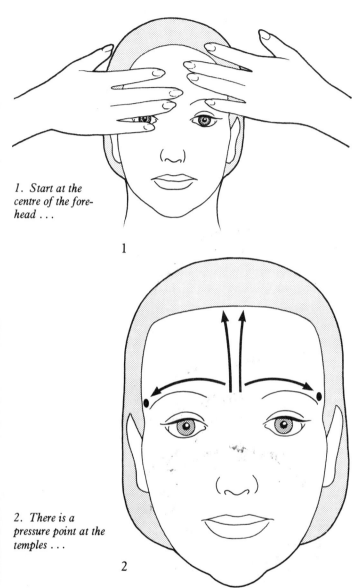

1. Start at the centre of the fore-head . . .

1

2. There is a pressure point at the temples . . .

2

Massage with everything

Let me remind you again of Celia's Second Law: *Never do only one thing if you can do two at the same time*. Massage, which is beneficial for every type of skin, provides the perfect opportunity. Every time you cleanse your face or tone it, every time you nourish it, you can give yourself a brief massage.

There will be some high days in your life when you can steal an hour or so for a really leisurely facial. You might even splurge once in a while with a massage in a salon. It's a super-sybaritic thing to do, surpassed for sheer, satisfying self-indulgence only by a body massage. However, there is one important thing to bear in mind if you are getting ready for a special occasion. A vigorous professional massage can be extremely stimulating. It will rouse your circulation and may even bring out a latent bump or two. Afterwards, your face should rest before you make it up. So if you're counting on a salon massage for, say, your wedding day when you're apt to be excited anyway and prone to spots, have it done a week or even two weeks in advance, and not the day before.

As with a body massage, you will pick up useful techniques from the professional. With a little practice, even if you never enter a salon, you can educate your fingers to become pretty proficient at home. Here is how.

All your movements must be upwards (except down the bony ridge of your nose). Upward movements support the skin, rather than dragging it down. You use only the two centre fingers of each hand (not the index finger, because it is too strong, nor the little finger, because it is too weak). You move them gently, smoothly and slowly, using both hands.

Dip your fingertips into whatever it is you are applying. Oils or creams make them slide easily and help the massage to do its work. Start at the centre of the forehead, just above the bridge of the nose, and using your two hands alternately, slightly overlapping them as you go, work vertically on the forehead up to the hairline. Then move horizontally across the forehead, each hand working separately and gradually outwards. There is a pressure point at the temples where both hands pause simultaneously. Exert just the slightest bit of pressure, not hard, but firm enough to be aware

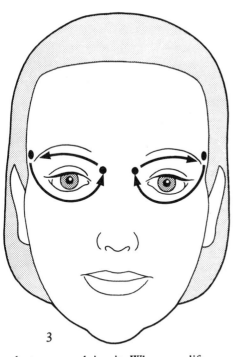

3

3. Move around and under your eyes . . .

4. Go down the ridge of the nose . . .

4

that you are doing it. When you lift your fingers, you will feel a slight sensation of relief, of relaxation.

Repeat this as many times as you like. Remember, every stroke is not only stimulating your skin, but also helping to counteract wrinkles.

Next, using *only* the middle finger of each hand, move around and under your eyes, upwards and *always* towards the nose, *never* away from it. Trace a path up into the sockets above your eyes, and then move outwards, on the upper lids, *towards* the temples. Smoothly and gently. Never abruptly. When you have finished, let your fingers trail away. Again, repeat as many times as you like.

Now go down the ridge of the nose, once more using the centre fingers of both hands alternately, in continuous sweeping movements. Next, the sides of the nose. Here the motion is a continuous series of tiny circles. The general direction is downwards, starting at the bridge, but the pressure comes each time your fingers begin the *upward* circle.

5. The sides of the nose

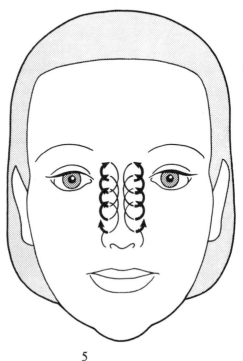

5

*6. The corners of
the nose*

7. The cheeks

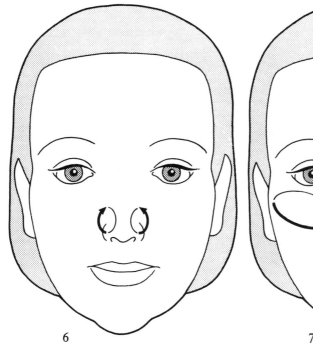

6

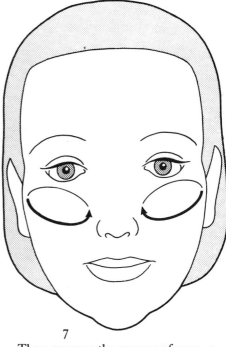

7

*8. Where lines form
leading down from
the nose*

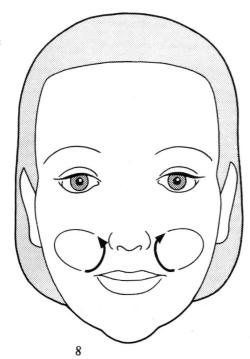

8

Then massage the corners of your
nose, rubbing lightly, repeatedly, with
the same circular movement. Take time
over this, especially if you have any
problems such as blackheads. You will
pull funny faces when you do it. You are
supposed to. It helps to strengthen the
muscles.

The cheeks come next. With one hand
on each side, move from your ears
upward, along the cheekbones. Make
certain that you don't come anywhere
near the eyes. If you do, you may well
drag the skin beneath them downwards.
This, I repeat, is what you always want
to avoid. You perform a circular movement around your cheeks, but you exert
pressure *only* as your fingers move
upwards. On the way down, let your
fingers trail.

Do the same, working over the area
where the lines form leading down from
the nose. As before, broad circular
sweeps, moving gradually downwards,
but *pressure only on the way up*. When
you approach the mouth, finish off with

light flicks above the lips, one hand at a time. Depending on the space between the upper lip and the nose, you can use either the two usual massage fingers or the middle finger alone.

Last, the neck and the jawline. Here you use only one hand at a time, the right on the left side, and vice versa. Turn your head to one side, stretching your chin forward as far as you can, so that the skin beneath it becomes taut. Starting from the centre of the collarbone, work upwards under the chin and along the jawbone. Then, upwards on the neck to the ears. Trail your fingers away. Turn your head in the other direction, and do the same. Then again. And again and again, if you like.

Complicated as all that may sound, it will soon become an automatic part of your daily routine.

There are times when you will want to massage more completely, to give your skin extra nourishment or stimulation. Using the appropriate cream or lotion, go four or five times through all the procedures I have just described. Then, repeat them all several times over, but now change the style of finger-movement slightly.

Instead of using long continuous strokes, you move your fingers only about half an inch at a time. Pause. Move another half-inch. And so on. This exerts a firmer, slightly more stimulating pressure. It is valuable for all of us, and particularly so for those of us trying to ward off wrinkles around our mouths.

There is one more technique that you can use at home. It is known as 'tapoting', from the French word, *tapoter*, to pat. You follow the same patterns, moving in the same directions, over forehead, around eyes and cheeks, under the chin and up the neck. But now, despite what I said earlier, you use three fingers, the index, the centre and the ring. There is no danger in this, however, because the pressure you exert is so slight.

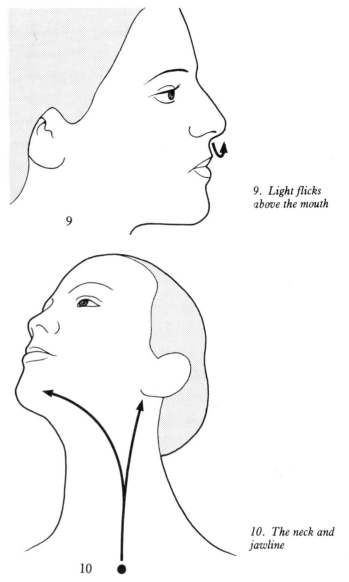

9. *Light flicks above the mouth*

10. *The neck and jawline*

Tapping lightly and quickly with the pads of all three, one after the other, and using both hands, you pat-pat-pat all over your face. It should feel as gentle as raindrops falling. Tapoting is particularly good for the tender skin under your eyes.

A word of warning: do not tapot if you have very long fingernails.

5. Make-up 1: basic principles – face-shapes, contouring, shading, blushing and highlighting

Some people call make-up the art of illusion. Others, more cynical, say it is delusion, sheer fakery, in fact. I know from years of practising the art that it is a little bit of both.

Make-up creates an illusion by fibbing ever so slightly about both good features and bad. The point of it is not to try to create an entirely *different* face, but to make the face you have look as good as nature could have made it – and should have – if only nature had been a little more considerate.

Few women are born with perfect faces. Those we think of as perfect (models and film stars) have a head-start on the rest of us, of course. But their impact – what we call their beauty – often depends less on what they were born with than on the skill with which they have been dramatized.

You might be astonished if you were to see some of them with their faces naked, before their defects have been concealed or modified. A 'perfect' beauty with one eye slightly larger than the other? With a thin, almost shapeless, upper lip? With spots on her skin? Far more often than you would imagine.

To such women, make-up, together with the help they get from cleverly contrived lighting and sophisticated camera work, becomes the means through which they project a clearly stated personality. The personality, however, is not necessarily their own. A hoyden today, a sweet-faced schoolgirl tomorrow – make-up for them is a mask.

That is the chief difference between them and you.

You are always projecting *yourself*. Make-up should never be a mask for you to hide behind. It should not be a transformation – rather an expression of what and who you are. Obviously, you would like it to be you at your very best. Not a copy of someone else. Not you trying to fit into a stereotype. Not you aping a 'fashionable' look that isn't you at all.

Fads in make-up come and go: heavy eyelines one year, thinly plucked eyebrows the next; pale lips one year, vividly red ones the next. No matter how the fashions chop and change, there is one look that is right for most of us most of the time. That is the natural look – you, but enhanced.

Now, I know that almost every woman who picks up this book – whether you are fifteen or fifty-plus – has put on make-up. Maybe regularly. Maybe only once in a while. I am well aware that I am not leading you into uncharted seas.

I am also certain that at some time or other you have been befuddled, frustrated or furious. You worked hard on your eyes, and they looked ghoulish instead of glamorous. Your foundation caked. Your lipstick smeared.

If you are new to make-up, you may not have known exactly what to expect from your products, or how best to use them. If you have been at it for years, you may have fallen into some bad habits without realizing it.

So I am going to start from the very beginning. It could be that everything you do is right. It is more likely that at least some of the things you do would benefit by change. Try, as you read this, to put any set ideas you have out of your head. Approach make-up as though you had never made up in your life.

Before you ever put so much as a blob of anything on your face, you must know why you are doing it. In my classes I often ask my students to pause and do a 'why' check:

'Why am I putting blue eyeshadow close to the brow?'
'Why am I using a deep beigy foundation?'
'Why am I highlighting the chin?'

If they don't have a good reason, or if they offer a really bad one like, 'I saw somebody else do it,' I ask them to stop. And think. And start again.

The same applies to you, sitting at your own dressing-table. If you don't know why you're doing a particular thing, don't do it. You could come seriously unstuck. You must be certain in advance of what you want to accomplish. To do that, you must know your face.

Confront it frankly, in a *clear, truthful, unflattering light* – the only sort of light in which you should ever try to make up. Daylight is best, shining towards you. Otherwise, electric light that is bright and evenly balanced. You want to dazzle, delight and deceive everyone else – but not yourself.

You will already have peered hard when you took your personal inventory (Chapter 2). What did you jot down? 'Nose detestable'? 'Forehead too high'? 'Ugly mole on cheek'? Be certain that these *are* faults before you try to disguise them. It could be that the very feature you hate is the one that lends your face that quality beyond price – character. Your nose may be a 'beak' to you, but appear 'aristocratic' to others. Your high

forehead, to a friend with a hairline too close to her eyes, is a 'noble brow' which makes her green with envy. As for moles, models sometimes stick on false ones, high on one cheek, perhaps, just for fun, or to cover an annoying spot. The effect can be very appealing.

Not long ago, I heard that glorious lady Lauren Bacall talking about her beginnings in Hollywood. No sooner was her contract signed than she was whisked down to be scrutinized by the make-up experts. 'Aha,' they said, 'we'll trim your eyebrows to even them up; they're very lopsided. We'll have caps put on your crooked teeth. And we'll pluck some hair off your forehead to give you a better hairline.'

Practically in tears, she rushed back to the producer who had discovered her. He promptly sent a command to the make-up department: 'Leave her alone. I hired her because she doesn't look like every other starlet in town. I want her just the way she is – lopsided eyebrows, crooked teeth and all!'

Of course, we're not all Miss Bacalls, and if you have one feature which makes you genuinely miserable you might want to consider cosmetic surgery. I personally feel that cutting and stitching your face should be reserved only for the most extreme circumstances. It is expensive and often painful. What is more, the results are irrevocable. Your new short nose could make you even more unhappy than your old long one. It may not 'match' the rest of you nearly so well, but now it's yours, and you're stuck with it.

As for face lifts, there is no question about it that having your wrinkles surgically tucked up will make your skin look firmer and younger. After a few years, alas, it will sag once more, and you will have to have it done all over again. And again after that. Is it worth it? Some say yes. I'm not so sure. Growing old is a natural and dignified process. Of course a woman should never give up trying to

shadow brushes   eye liner   lipstick brushes   eyebrow brush   mascara brush   blusher   powder brush

look her best – her best, that is, for her age. But it is futile (and I think foolish) to fight eternally to try to look younger than your years. A buoyant attitude of mind does more to keep a woman's appearance youthful than does an entire battery of costly cosmetic aids.

So – back to make-up and how to use it. In time you will learn to cope with your features, the good, the bad and the eccentric. You will learn to understate by day (who wants to look like Desdemona on the 8.15?) and to dramatize yourself by night when the disco lights flash and change or the dinner-table candles cast a soft, golden glow.

Put a little make-up on every day. Not only will it keep you looking good all the time, but with every repetition you will be adding to your expertise – toning colours ever more gently and imperceptibly, controlling your brushes and applicators with more skill.

You will soon discover (if you don't already know it) that you cannot make up effectively without the proper tools. I will list all the essentials in

Chapter 8. By then, I will have explained the function of each.

A good set of brushes is a worthwhile investment – for your face, for your eyes, for your lips. They should have long handles, which give you far better balance than short ones. The best are rather costly (sable hairs for small ones; sable or badger for large ones), but if you take care of them, they will last you many years. It is a waste of money to buy cheap nylon brushes. They fight you; they don't help you. They fall apart, they trail strands, and they are generally exasperating.

Most large chemist shops and departmental stores sell sets in assorted shapes and sizes which will meet almost any challenge. If your budget won't allow a full set at a single go, still insist upon good ones. Buy them, as you can afford them, one at a time.

When you first begin to take pains with your make-up, you will probably need at least a quarter of an hour for your daytime look, and half an hour or more to produce a glamorous, beautifully contoured, shaded and highlighted evening face. As you grow more proficient, you should be able to cut the time by half.

When you make up, tuck your hair back, so that you don't get creams or powders on it. If you have just had a wondrous new hair-do, carefully pin back the bits that touch your face, disturbing the style as little as possible. Ordinarily, you can keep it well out of the way with a fabric-covered elastic hairband (uncovered elastic may split the hairs), or with a couple of combs or hair clips.

Before you start, know how your hair will look afterwards. Will it cover your ears or forehead (or both)? If so, it will change your face-shape slightly. It will also cast shadows. You will want to bear all this in mind as you make up.

Basic principles

Make-up, like painting, depends for its effect on highlights and shadows. You highlight something that you want to draw attention to. You shade away what you want to minimize. *Good features highlighted; bad features shaded*. Thus, you accentuate good cheekbones or browbones with light make-up, draw attention away from a double chin or a broad nose with dark. You can also, with dark make-up, create hollows where they do not exist, but where you would like them, as in your cheeks.

The secret is subtlety. Nature abhors the hard, stark line and so must make-up. Take a zebra or a tabby cat. From the distance their stripes are clearly and sharply defined. Study them closely, and you will see that the stripes blend softly at the edges, that the brown-black hairs mingle with the white-beige ones. The varying tones smudge into each other. So it must be with make-up. Blending. Smudging. No sharp lines, no hard edges, whether you are highlighting, shading or applying colour.

I shall, in the pages that follow, use words like 'gently', 'smoothly', 'softly' and 'lightly' again and again. I am sorry about that. But I would rather run the risk of being repetitive than fail to make my point. Make-up is a subtle art. To succeed it must be subdued. And you must treat your face considerately.

The products with which you mould the contours are the *highlighter*, the *blusher*, and the *shaper* or *shader*. (Manufacturers don't make life easy when they call these by different names.) The highlighter is always lighter than your own skin tone, and therefore lighter than your foundation. (It may indeed *be* a lighter foundation.) The shader is darkish and browny. The blusher, which is reddish, pinky or tawny, not only helps to emphasize the shape you have created, but adds drama, warmth and colour.

If you have dark brown or black skin you must be certain that the shades you select are dark enough and vivid enough to show up against your complexion. You can be daring. Frosted products and products flecked with gold (for eyes and lips, as well as cheeks) can look stunning on you, where they might seem garish on paler faces.

Shaping and blushing is done either immediately after you have applied your foundation or after you have powdered (see Chapter 6). If you choose to do it at the foundation stage, you must use products similar in texture to the foundation, either in cream form or in liquid. If you choose to shape afterwards, then you must use brush-on powdery products. Most people prefer to shape, blush and shadow with powders. They are simpler to use; mistakes are easier to correct, and they are in general more flexible. Should you use too much, you can simply tone it all down with translucent face powder.

There are, as you will see, however, certain 'repairs', such as covering spots, broken veins or other blemishes, and concealing bags or lines, which are best done at the foundation stage.

Whichever you choose for shaping, remember this rule: *cream on cream and powder on powder. You cannot blend a powder into a creamy product. Or vice versa.* To try is to produce only misery patches.

If you contour with powder, you will need two brushes, one fairly broad, for shading and blushing; the other slightly smaller, for highlighting (see Chapter 8).

Face-shapes: contouring, shading, blushing and highlighting

Peas are round and eggs are oval. The definitions are precise and predictable. If only the same were true of faces! Not only do faces come in a variety of basic shapes, but in a vast variety of combinations of these. Most of us are put together like pieces in an identikit drawing – a forehead from one face-shape, cheeks from another, a chin from still a third.

Whenever I give make-up demonstrations, women come up and ask me, 'What face-shape am I?' I can seldom give them a straight, simple answer: heart-shaped, triangular or round. Like them you are probably not quite certain because your face, like theirs, is probably a mixture. Study other people's faces on buses and tubes. It is fascinating to break down the sections and to determine how disparate bits from several different shapes combine to produce one single relatively harmonious whole. Analysing other people's faces helps you to identify your own face-shape, or combination.

There are, of course, a few general outlines to which we all more or less conform. The diagrams that follow illustrate these, with suggestions on how best to flatter each with shapers, blushers and highlighters. The same principles apply whether you shape and shade with creams or with powders. In every case, you will play down your worst features and contour your face to make the best of your 'bonus' features – high cheekbones, a well-shaped chin, dimples, excellent eyes or a pretty mouth.

Some women like to do their eyes (see Chapter 7) before they contour their faces. Why not, if it works for them? I myself think it's better to face-shape first – but fairly lightly. Then make up your eyes. Have a good look at yourself. If the balance is not quite right, if your eyes seem over-dominant, intensify shader, blusher and/or highlighter – whichever is needed.

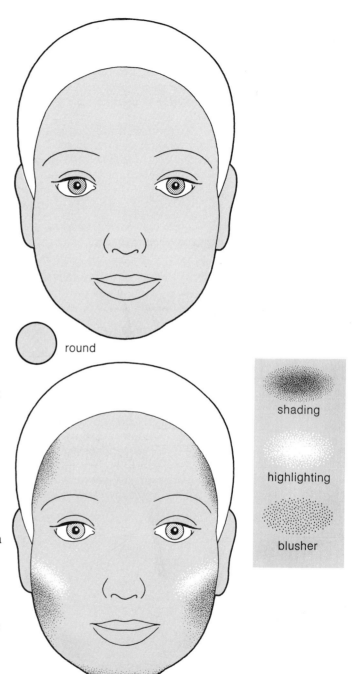

round

shading

highlighting

blusher

Round face

This is usually a chubby, child-like face
with generous cheeks. It is often dim-
pled. It may accompany overweight, but
not necessarily. The features in general
need to be sharpened and fined down,
and the overall outline slimmed, especially at the chin and jaws.

Give yourself a head-start by using
two foundations, a fairly dark shade on
the outer parts of your face and at the
chin-line, and a lighter shade on the
centre panel. This helps to break up the
broad fleshy areas and to make the width
seem to recede. Blend the two shades
into each other imperceptibly.

Create hollows in the cheeks with
shader, and highlight the cheekbones to
create a further illusion of slimness. Be
extremely wary of using a blusher on the
cheeks. You may be able to get away
with the *merest hint* of colour if you are
pale; more than that will make your
round cheeks look even rounder. If possible, avoid a blusher entirely.

58

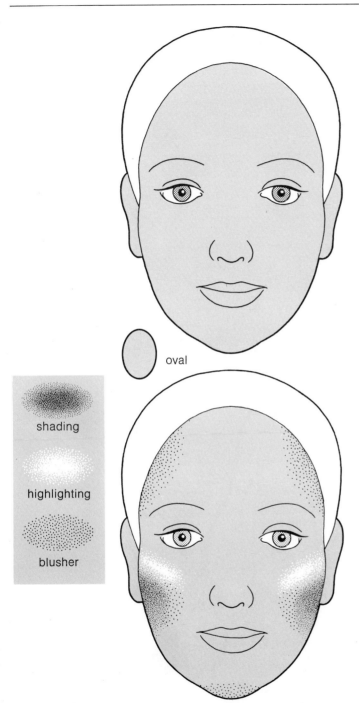

oval

shading

highlighting

blusher

Oval face

This, at its best, is an enviable face. It is long and rounded, both at the temples and at the jawline, and the width at the top tapers gradually down to the chin. It is usually well balanced and, especially if it is accompanied by high cheekbones, may need little in the way of re-shaping.

The oval face, however, can sometimes exaggerate its own good lines. The forehead may be slightly too broad for the rest of the face, and there may be too great an expanse between the eyebrows and the hairline. The distance between the bottom lip and the chin may also be over-long.

You break up long lines and large blank areas with the blusher; create hollows in the cheeks with the shader, and highlight the cheekbones. Play up both your eyes and your mouth. Attention-getting eyes and a soft, brow-concealing hair style (Chapter 9) draw attention away from the high forehead. A well-shaped, attractively-coloured mouth counteracts the length between the lower lip and the chin.

59

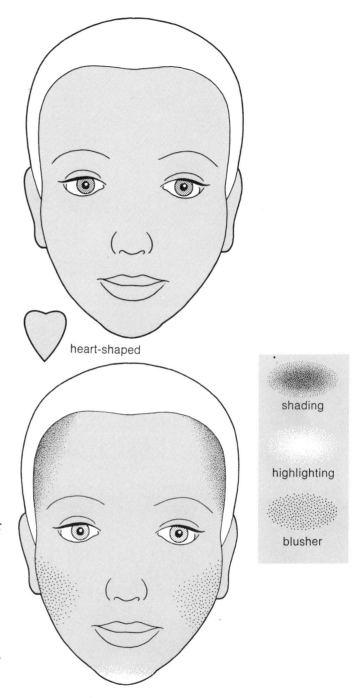

heart-shaped

shading

highlighting

blusher

Heart-shaped face

Writers always claim that the heart-shaped face is ideal. This face is extremely attractive – broad at the temples and appealingly narrow (almost kittenlike) at the chin.

It usually tends to be small and rather delicate, so it can't afford to have too many tricks played on it; there simply isn't the space. Too much make-up can, in fact, detract from its piquancy.

You want to make certain that the balance is good between the comparatively broad forehead and the smallish chin. This means shading your temples and underplaying your eyes slightly (unless they are magnificent, and demand the right to overpower all else). Hollow your cheeks, if necessary; use comparatively vivid colour on your mouth, and highlight your chin.

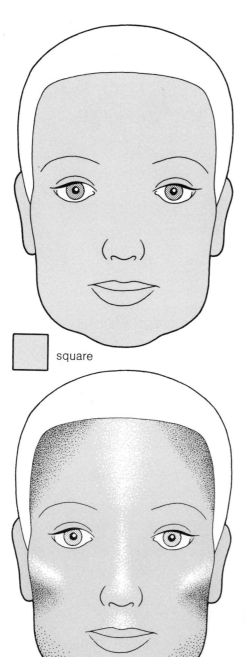

square

shading

highlighting

blusher

Square face

This face is composed of equal distances, the width at the temples and the jaw and the height from the hairline to the bottom of the chin all being approximately the same. It is usually a large face with strong features. The features may be individually very attractive, but they must be balanced by shading and blushing so that one does not dominate the others.

The overall impression is of too much width and too little height – a squat effect. Counteract this by highlighting the centre panel, the cheekbones and the chin, and by shadowing fairly heavily at the temples, the outer extremities of the jawline and in the hollows of the cheeks.

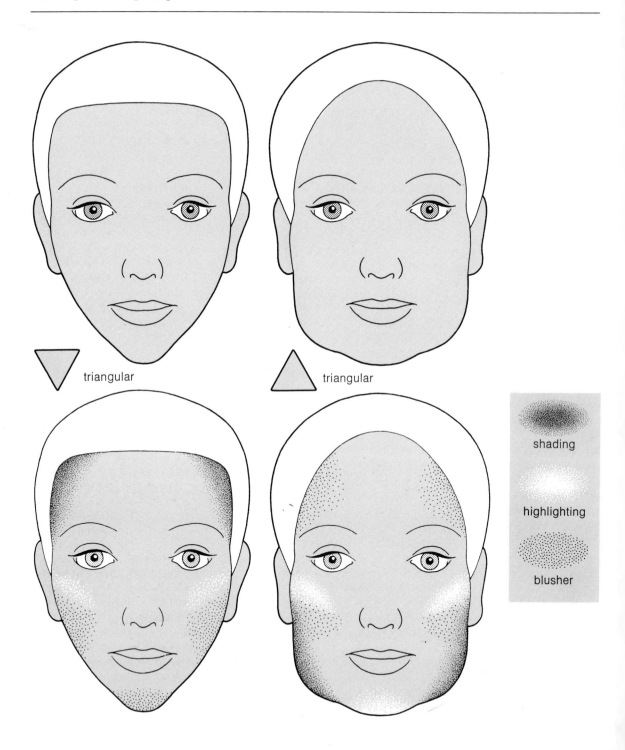

triangular

triangular

shading

highlighting

blusher

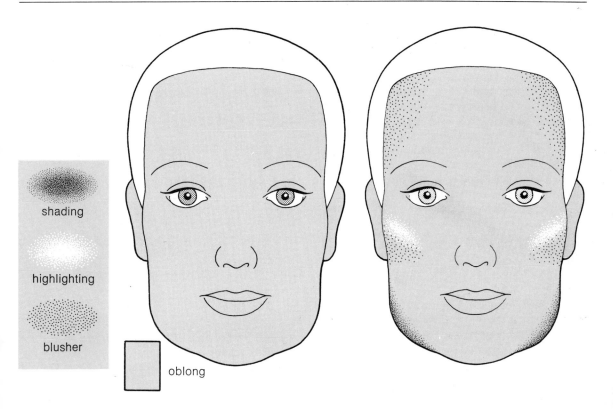

shading

highlighting

blusher

oblong

Triangular face

A face can be triangular either with very broad temples and a sharply-pointed chin or, more rarely, with a comparatively narrow forehead and a broad chin. The first is similar to the heart-shaped face, but with more angular lines. The entire face needs softening to achieve a gentle, pretty effect. The temples are shaded to make them appear less broad, and the chin is shaded to shorten it. Beware of highlighters. Use no more than the faintest touch on the cheekbones, and then only if they are not very broad.

The upside-down-triangle, with a narrow forehead and a broad angular jaw, must be softened in reverse. The sides of the jaw are narrowed by shading, the temples broadened with a blusher, and the cheekbones and chin emphasized with a highlighter.

Oblong face

This is either a long version of the square face or an angular version of the oval. It is a rewarding shape on which to work, since there is plenty of space for either dramatic or subtle effects. It often has good high cheekbones and wide areas between the eyes and the brows.

The most important corrections are softening the angles at the temples and the jawline with shader. The eyes and the mouth can both be played up. The hollows in the cheeks should not be too heavily shadowed. It is better to suggest hollows with a dark blusher than with a shader, and to highlight the cheekbones in compensation.

Mixed faces – an example: the square/oval

As I said at the start, few people have a clear-cut face-shape. If yours is a mixture, study the contouring diagrams for the two (or even three) shapes which you may combine. Then use the suggestions that apply to you. Look carefully at the relationship between your eyes and your eyebrows; between your brows and your hairline; between your bottom lip and your chin; between the width at the forehead and the width at the jaw. Then make the necessary corrections.

Emphasize what is good. Shade away what displeases you.

A few special notes for special effects

A very small face looks larger with a lighter foundation on the outsides of the cheeks and at the temples.

A very large face looks smaller with a darker foundation on the outsides of the cheeks and at the temples.

A broad and/or high forehead can be diminished with a blusher. For too much width, break up the space with a blusher at the sides of the temples. For too much height, use blusher in the centre, between the brows.

Small eyelids appear larger with a lighter foundation almost up to the brow. This opens up the entire area.

Eyes set too wide apart can be brought closer together by darkening both sides of the bridge of the nose (either with foundation or shader).

Bags and shadows under the eyes are faded away with a lighter foundation.

Crows' feet, furrows in the brow and deep lines from nose to mouth and from mouth to chin are faded away with a lighter foundation.

A broad nose can be slimmed by shading (either with a darker foundation or a shader) down the sides of the nose, and by highlighting (either with a lighter

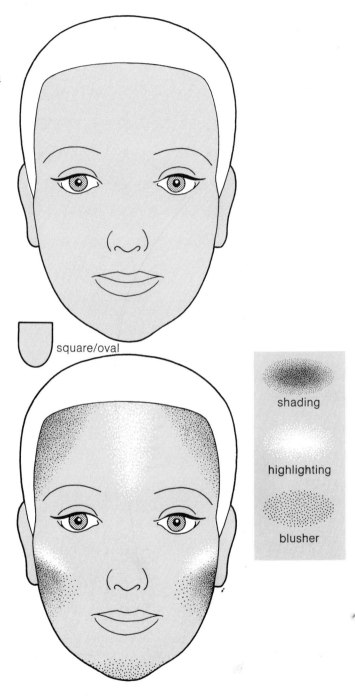

square/oval

shading

highlighting

blusher

64

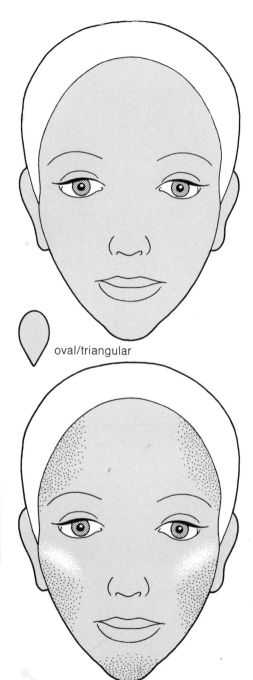

oval/triangular

shading

highlighting

blusher

foundation or a powder highlighter) down the centre.

A long nose can be shortened with a touch of dark (shader or foundation) under the tip.

A double chin can be made to look less chubby by shading the bulgy bits (with darker foundation or shader).

A long chin is shortened by darkening the tip (with a touch of darker foundation, shader or blusher).

A chin lacking clearly-defined contours can be given a more definite shape with a touch of shading (darker foundation or shader) in the centre, to suggest a cleft, or slightly higher – nearer the lip – to create a little valley. Of course, you can do both.

A narrow lower lip can be made to look fuller with a touch of shading directly below it (darker foundation or shader).

Hollows in the cheeks are formed either with a darker foundation or a shader. The shading should begin just under the upper jawbone and move gradually from the ear forward and down onto the cheeks. This is where the shadow falls with cheeks which are naturally concave. The effect is enhanced by highlighting the cheekbones (with lighter foundation or highlighter).

Very dark blushers can often be substituted for shaders – on the temples, the forehead, the cheekbones and the chin.

One last important word

All of the above must be done with exquisite finesse. Drastic corrections may prove too conspicuous for daywear. Bright daylight could make what were meant to be hollows in the cheeks look like dirty, brownish smudges. So proceed with caution. If the changes you plan are highly dramatic, better restrict them to evening use when soft lighting is your ally.

6. Make-up 2: foundations and powder

Foundations

A foundation is precisely what the word says. It is the base upon which all else you do depends. The foundation, more than anything, is what makes the difference between a woman who is beautifully groomed and one who is not. That enviable look, that apparent smoothness of skin, is, ninety-nine times out of a hundred, the result of a foundation properly applied.

Women sometimes say to me, 'I don't like to look made up, so I don't wear a foundation at all.' That is a grave mistake. After about the age of twelve, almost every skin needs a bit of help, a bit of cheering up. Foundations can be exceedingly light in texture, so filmy as to be almost invisible. They need not (in fact, should not) be something that you have obviously slodged on.

If your skin is remarkably good, you may not want to wear a foundation all the time over your entire face. You may choose to skip one entirely when you have a tan. But ordinarily, almost everyone benefits by wearing at least a little, if nowhere else, then down the centre of the face, especially on the nose. (We all say it, even those of us with dry skin: 'I'm sorry. I must go and powder my nose.' That isn't just a euphemism.)

A foundation overlays tiny blemishes, conceals irregularities and dark shadows (as under the eyes) and makes your skin glow and look alive. Equally important, it actually protects the skin – from pollu-tion in the atmosphere, from cold winds and from blazing sun.

For daywear, you will ask of your foundation chiefly that it flatter you as much as possible and that it help you make the best of your features. For evening, you will use it more adven-turously. You will probably experiment, and discover the impact of a darker shade. You may, once you know what you're about, use a lighter one to block out entire areas, just as an artist does on a canvas, and then, with deeper tones, gradually create a vivid, well-contoured facial picture.

Day or night, you will not always want to do exactly the same thing. If you are looking jaded, you may want to warm your complexion with a hint of russet, a tint of peach. Or you may choose to vary your appearance to match a mood or an occasion – pale and mys-terious this evening; robust and hearty tomorrow.

The right foundation

You select your foundation to suit your skin type, your natural colouring and your general needs. If your skin is clear and trouble-free, you can get away with a very fine foundation; if it is blemished, you will need one that is heavier and more concealing. Foundations are – or should be – carefully labelled for normal, dry or oily skin. (Where no skin-type is specified, it is usually meant for 'normal'.) If you don't choose the right one, everything you do afterwards can go ludicrously wrong. With a combination skin, it is wise to use two different foundations, one for oily in the centre panel; one for dry or normal on the rest of your face.

Most foundations are cream- or oil-based, and can be bought in cream form, packed in jars; compressed into cakes, in compacts; in liquid, either in bottles or tubes; formed into sticks like oversized lipsticks, or, more rarely, in aerosols, which squirt it out in a mousse, like shaving cream. The sticks are almost always heavier, more covering, than the others; the aerosols tend to be filmy.

Water-based foundations are also available. These are designed for extremely oily skins and produce a matt finish, a surface which looks as if it has already been powdered. They often separate into liquid and sediment in the bottle, and must be well shaken before they are applied. You can also buy water-based glosses and tints, either in liquid form or in gel. They look a bit frightening in their bottles or tubes, because they are extremely dark (as dark say, as brown ale).

You stroke them over your face very, very thinly with dampened cotton wool, and the result is suntan-like. They are not meant, of course, to be worn constantly, day after day, but they can be helpful (to normal and dry skin, as well as to oily) when your holiday tan is beginning to fade. It is these, by the way, which men – you know, the 'machismo' type – sometimes wear.

It doesn't really matter whether you choose a liquid, a cream, a foam or a stick. All achieve the same result, but you may find one or the other a little easier to work with, a little more responsive, a little better suited to the nature of your skin.

As for colour, all of the big-name brands offer a wide selection, from the palest to the darkest, usually a choice of at least eight, and sometimes as many as

ten. There are invariably two that are extremely light, one tending towards the ivory, the other towards the pink; two medium, one on the beige side, the other, warmer and pinker; and two that are fairly dark, one rusty-tan, the other, a yellowish, deep beige. In addition, you will probably find something in the same range that is quite definitely peach.

Cosmetics manufacturers have at long last begun to cater not only for the so-called white complexion, but for oriental, brown and black skins, as well. It may take a little searching, but whatever your colour, you should be able to find what you need.

How do you decide, among the galaxy of shades available, which is the one for you? Again, it is a matter of staring at yourself. Study your face closely and you will be able to discern a natural pinkness or creaminess or beigeness. It will help to look at the skin just above your wrist on the inside of your arm; the tone there is usually much the same as it is on your face. But not invariably – so be sure.

It will also help to flip through the clothes in your wardrobe. If you often buy pastel blues and pinks, you probably have a delicate English-rose skin. If your wardrobe is filled with greens and browns, you are likely to be darker, more russety. If you see red on hanger after hanger, your skin is probably sallow, and in need of a lift. 'I love that colour,' you will have said. 'It looks good on me.' Instinct has led you to make the most of your natural complexion.

A foundation should be in your own true skin tone, and no more than either one shade lighter or darker. (Black-skinned ladies must never go even one shade lighter; the difference will always show.) If you vary further than one shade up or down, you can look extremely unmatched, with a face that seems to belong to one person and hands, arms and as much of your bosom as shows seeming to belong to quite another.

Should you sometimes, for kicks, decide to become Miss Hawaii or Miss Lapland (very dark or very light on your face), then watch out. You must be ready to counter the problems that will ensue. It could mean either a high-necked, long-sleeved, all-concealing dress or the nuisance of body make-up.

So – you're ready to treat yourself to a new foundation. It need not be the most expensive on the market. The less costly lines can be equally effective and, especially if you are experimenting with something entirely new, I would certainly recommend that you start at the lower end of the price range.

You have defined your requirements. You know what you want your foundation to do. Remember, the sales assistant has never set eyes on you before; she knows far less about you than you do yourself. She *could* be absolutely super and experienced and full of sound advice. But the chances are just as good that this is the first day in her life she has ever stood behind a cosmetics counter. In any case, you will probably be wearing make-up when you go out to shop, and there is absolutely no way she can tell what your skin is like underneath. So don't depend on her. Depend on you.

It is your money. Spend it cannily. Take it slow and easy. Ask to sample the colours available. Try a bit of several shades – not on the back of your hand, but on the skin inside your arm, which you have already checked to be sure that it matches your face. And beware of shop lighting; some can distort colours seriously. Step out into the daylight to study the true shades of your sample dabs.

Just because you are buying a new foundation, don't throw your old, partly used ones away – not, that is, unless colour or texture have proved an absolute disaster. If so, admit your mistakes and chuck them out. But if the texture is right, hold on to them. They stay good

for years; they must be utterly ancient before they go rancid. Differing shades always come in handy. You can use two for special effects – light in the centre, for instance, and dark at the sides, to slim your cheeks. If you are just plain practical, you can lighten a dark one or darken a light one by mixing several drops or blobs of the one into the other. For a liquid, add the dark or the light little by little to the bottle; shake well, and keep adding until you get the shade you want. For a cream, mix the two in the palm of your hand each time you apply.

On its own, an odd shade is valuable too. The light one that you bought last winter when you were pale – or chose misguidedly – is useful as a highlighter (look back at the face-shape diagrams, pp. 58–65) or to obscure shadows. In any case, you may be pale again in three months. Save the dark one you bought the last time you were tanned for next summer's tan.

A note on this, by the way: if you like to wear a foundation during the evening when you are on holiday, buy your bronzy one before you leave home; a small or remote beach resort is the last place you are likely to find your favourite product.

If you don't want your face to tan at all, but only your body (many models do this), be sure you take along a supply of a sunny-looking foundation with a built-in barrier that screens out the burning ultra-violet rays. And don't forget a broad-brimmed hat.

Before I go into detail on how to apply your foundation, I want to discuss a few skin problems that should be dealt with at the foundation stage.

Extremely oily skin

Oiliness and shininess go together, and between them they make it difficult for a foundation to stick. The solution is first to apply an anti-shine liquid or gel.

These are formulated to prevent the oiliness from coming through to the surface. They will, therefore, encourage your foundation to stay where you put it. Unless your condition is drastic, you will probably have to use anti-shine on the centre panel only.

Redness

Unnaturally high colour, blotches and broken veins – anything that shows red on your face – can be persuaded to disappear by using a green foundation under your normal one. Green counteracts the redness. Manufacturers usually tag these by some such name as 'mint' or 'peppermint'. You apply them (following the instructions below for applying all foundations) only on the places where excess redness occurs, perhaps your nose or your cheeks. Have no fears. The degree of greenness is very slight, and you won't end up looking like Dracula's granny. Only rather pale. For the covering foundation, choose one with as much beige as your natural skin tone permits; beiges themselves also contain miniscule amounts of green, but no red.

If the splotches are not widespread (say, only a broken vein or two), you can solve the problem with two versions of your regular foundation colour, the second layer slightly heavier in consistency than the first. Use the thinner one all over your face. Then gently pat the heavier one on to the reddish places, taking great care to blend the edges so no lines of demarcation show.

Acne, spots, blemishes and cold sores

Women with serious acne should, of course, consult a dermatologist. It is nasty, annoying and tenacious, and definitely a medical problem. Acne can be concealed to some extent with a fairly thick *medicated* foundation. This helps to cure while it covers.

A small blemish or the occasional spot can be 'dotted' into invisibility with the same sort of medicated foundation or with a medicated coverstick, a thickish solid cream packaged like a lipstick. These should exactly match the foundation or be one tone lighter. Never darker. They are applied after the foundation.

For an infected spot of any kind, use a cotton swab to dot the covering product on. If you have a second spot, do not re-use the same bit of cotton. You will only spread the infection. Use the other end of the swab on the second go. If you have more to deal with after that, rip off the bits at the tips that have touched your skin, to reveal new clean cotton surfaces underneath. Even better, throw the swab away, and give yourself a new one.

You can, if you prefer, 'paint' over a tiny blemish or spot with an extremely fine brush, dipped into medicated foundation. Don't move on to a second spot without rinsing the brush in a mild antiseptic solution.

It is almost impossible to cover spots or pimples that have been attacked. So leave them alone. Don't pick at them or squeeze them. Once they get weepy, there is no way that foundation will adhere to them. It is also extremely difficult to cover cold sores. You can, however, do a bit of good to 'blind boils', those angry, shiny bumps which sometimes erupt when we are run-down, or during menstruation. Cover them with anti-shine liquid or gel (see note above for oily skin) before you put on your foundation.

Birthmarks and scars

One must acknowledge facts. If such marks are severe, they can be difficult to conceal. But nothing is impossible. With birthmarks, the problem is usually a matter of colour – red or brownish blotches – which must be blocked out or toned down. Specially thick foundations are made for this purpose. Apply one to the patch *only*, selecting either a beige or a very pale shade, depending on your skin-colour and the colour of the blotch. Cover lightly with translucent powder, and then, with the greatest possible delicacy, pat your regular foundation over this area when you do the rest of your face.

Scars which have left bumpy surfaces are more complicated to disguise. If they are accompanied by abnormal coloration, you can make them less conspicuous with heavy foundation, as above. Beyond that, the best way to cope is by making up the rest of your face cleverly, shaping and highlighting to draw attention away from the disfiguration and to direct it towards your best features.

This is not easy, I know. Problems vary from face to face, and even those of us who spend our lives dealing with make-up can achieve positive results only by experimenting, by trial and error.

Wax is sometimes applied to fill in gaps, with amazing results. This must be done professionally. The Red Cross provides a free service to help deal with concealing scars, and a leading manufacturer which specializes in cosmetics for medical and surgical problems will advise you on their use.

Applying foundation

I will repeat what I have said before. *You must start with an absolutely clean skin whenever you do an entirely fresh make-up.* Of course, you will touch up here and there during a long day or a long evening. But you cannot slap on layer upon layer of gunk, one over another. It looks ghastly. Not only that. If you make a habit of it, day after day, over a long period, it can eventually ruin your skin. So, you will have cleansed, toned and moisturized before you begin. Or, if it's morning and you cleansed

completely last night, you can go straight on to toning and moisturing.

There is one exception. Should you want your make-up to remain friendly, flattering and faithful for an exceptionally long time (a business conference, with no chance to pop out for a quick repair; or a wedding, and you're the bride), then miss out on the moisturizer. *Foundation lasts longer on a toned skin.* You may need a tiny amount of moisturizer to deal with wrinkles under the eyes. Otherwise, skip it entirely.

And a note for those with *exceedingly dry skin.* You will, of course, use a foundation with a built-in moisturizer. But you can be doubly kind to yourself. When you apply your regular moisturizer, don't massage it in completely, but leave a thin film on the surface. The two layers of moisturizer will mingle, adding extra lubrication to the surface and extra retension of the natural moisture beneath your skin.

In every other respect, we all follow the same rules for putting on foundation. Allowing plenty of time for this pays dividends. A few minutes extra in the morning can save endless retouching all the rest of the day.

You start with clean fingertips, taking the foundation either directly from the container or from a blob in the palm of your hand. Work quickly and lightly. You are *not*, as with cleansers, toners and moisturizers, massaging the product into your skin. To do so is only to massage it deeply (and harmfully) into the pores. With foundations, you concentrate only on the surface. You do, however, move your fingers in the same general, beneficial patterns that you employ in massage: upward rather than downward; never against the uplifting action of the muscles; never dragging down.

Be aware of any soft, downy hairs you may have on your face. Pat the foundation over them in the direction in which

they naturally lie. To go against their grain is like brushing velvet in the wrong direction.

Now, I said fingertips. Many people feel confident of what they are doing only when they touch their skin directly with their own hands. So put your foundation on with your fingers, if you like. But, for a truly smooth finish, go over it all again with a slightly dampened sponge – a couple of inches in diameter and either natural or synthetic.

Personally, I prefer a sponge for the entire application. The result is infinitely more even and far longer lasting. What is more, using only a sponge, you avoid any risk of the fingers tending to massage. Some people even dip the sponge rather than their fingers directly into the foundation. Not a bad idea for doing the job well, but a little wasteful, a touch extravagant with the product.

To get your sponge to exactly the right degree of dampness, wet it thoroughly under the tap, squeeze it as dry as you can with your hands, then wrap it in a couple of layers of tissue and squeeze it again. Only a trace of mois-

ture is left. So barely moist is it that if you work slowly you may have to moisten it a second time. Your sponge will absorb make-up and soon become messy-looking. So you should wash it at least once a week (every couple of days or so is better), either in medicated soap or in an ordinary soap, followed by a rinse in a mild, odourless antiseptic solution. If your skin is spotty, wash it after every use.

Except with water-based products, which dry almost immediately and must be spread as they are applied, the easiest and most efficient procedure is to dab a few drops of foundation an inch or two apart on your face, taking one section at a time. Then blend them gently into each other with the sponge.

Start with the forehead and the temples, and go on to your eyelids – unless they need something special. If they do, hold off for a moment. Be careful not to drench your eyebrows. (You will have to brush the hairs clean when you come to pencilling them.) Cover your ear-lobes with foundation if they are over-red. Then move on to the cheeks, the jawline and the chin, shading away gradually as you reach your throat. Don't go all the way down onto your neck: the foundation will mark your clothes and, if you have wrinkles, it will accentuate rather than diminish them.

Look at yourself in the mirror, profile as well as head-on, to make certain that there are no abrupt lines where jawline and throat meet. Few make-up errors are more disconcerting than the mask-like look of a foundation that covers only the front of the face.

Now you are ready for the fiddly bits, the little traps where make-up deteriorates first: the corners of the eyes, the cracks around the nose, the cleft of the chin, the sensitive areas under the eyes, and the eyelids if they present any problems – blue veins, for instance, or wrinkles. Extra care in all these spots, and extra delicacy always near the eyes.

Blue-veined lids call for a slightly heavier foundation than you use on the rest of your face. Wrinkles above, below or beside the eyes, should have either a filmier foundation (thin enough not to pile up in the wrinkles), or your regular one applied in an infinitesimal quantity, and exceedingly gently, so as not to pull at the skin. In all these tricky places, you pat the foundation on lightly, rather than using a stroking motion. Whatever you do, you mustn't apply too much. The result is clogging, which in turn causes streaking before many hours have passed.

Now you have laid your base. This is the time to correct dark circles under your eyes, bags, lines from your nose to your mouth, furrows in your brow, crows' feet. Again, the words are 'carefully' and 'gently'. And again, we are dealing in fractional quantities. You pat on a foundation slightly lighter in shade than the one you have already used, and blend the two together with your sponge. *Only enough to cover.* Too much will make matters worse, not better.

If you are going to shape, shade and highlight with cream, do it now. (Have another look at the face-shape diagrams, pp. 58–65.) If you plan to do it afterwards with brush-on products, then you are ready to set your foundation with powder.

Powder

Every once in a while, some pundit will decree, 'This season it's chic to look shiny.' And a lot of sheep-like women will follow the leader and go shiny, whether it suits them or not. A few girls (usually young, and usually tanned) look fabulous without powder, especially in the summer, when it suggests being sporty and outdoorsy.

But most of us don't seem quite finished if we haven't powdered our faces. More important, powder makes everything that we have done at the

ONE GIRL – FOUR LOOKS

1. Simple day look

Very fine foundation matches skin colour. Eyes softly coloured with warm brown shadow; a little of same shadow under the eyes. Mascara top and bottom – not too much. Warm coral blusher matches lipstick, which was blotted before adding a little lip gloss. Hair kept simple – just a slight flick at the bottom ends.

2. Elegant day look

For a special lunch date – or maybe to counter the effects of an off day. Foundation a shade *paler* than skin, applied slightly more heavily under eyes (to disguise shadows) and on cheekbones. Eyes outlined in dark grey pencil softened at the corners – mascara applied a little more heavily. Blusher applied slightly lower down than on simple day look and a shade stronger and warmer. Because there's extra make-up on the eyes, a stronger and brighter colour on lips. Hair simply two plaits taken up and fixed with a slide.

3. Romantic evening look

Soft and dreamy. Foundation shade paler than skin. Soft mauve on outer corner of eyes blended upwards. Blue pencil on inner corner of top lid and underneath eyes is slightly smudged. Highlight down centre of lid – going up to centre of brow. Lots of mascara. Blusher under cheekbone to shape face, with soft pearly beige highlight on cheekbone above blusher. A touch of frosted highlighter dotted just above cupid's bow before drawing very firm lip-line. Hair set simply on heated rollers, then brushed out softly and loosely and caught in slide at side.

4. Glamorous evening look

Foundation shade lighter than skin. Face blotted with damp sponge after applying translucent powder and powdered again – to make it last through long, hot evenings. Dark grey shadow blended into socket and winged outwards, and charcoal liner along top of lashes blended upwards, with smudgy line of charcoal under eye. Frosted pearly highlighter under brows and on lids, with emphasis in centre. Brows defined here much more than in other pictures. Blusher applied under cheekbones – very warm colour, matching lips. Gloss on centre only of bottom lip. Hair set on ordinary medium rollers, dried and brushed out.

1

2

3

4

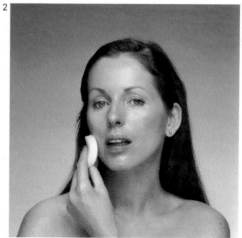

Step by Step to Beauty

1 made up, but
nothing to show for it

2 applying foundation
(as near to own skin
colour as possible) with
damp sponge

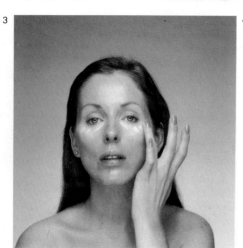
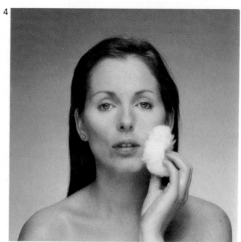

3 a slightly lighter
foundation under the
eyes for highlighting

4 applying powder
with powder puff

5 applying eye shadow
– dark rusty brown

6 lighter shadow (light
beige) added on lid and
brow

7 mascara –
brown/black – applied
top and bottom

8 eyebrow pencil –
brown and dark brown
mix

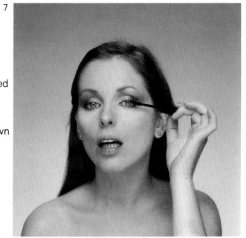

9 coral blusher

10 outlining mouth

11 filling in mouth –
warm russet

12 hair done and
ready to go . . .

1

2

BEFORE AND AFTER

For the not quite so young

The aim here is to brighten the overall look. So very fine foundation – either same colour as skin or shade darker. Slightly lighter shade under eyes. Translucent powder blotted with damp sponge after applying, to remove excess powder around wrinkles. Eyeshadow applied at outer corner of lids blended inwards and upwards, and highlighter added on brow bone to open up eyes. Blusher applied *on* cheekbone, not under (under would make face look gaunt) – and no highlighter on cheekbones (for same reason). The warm lipstick is not too shiny, since shiny lipsticks tend, in older ladies, to 'bleed' into lines round the mouth. Hair is swept upwards, blow-dried with tongs and brush.

For the young

An oblong face, with a tendency towards a square jaw. Eye make-up opens up the eyes and makes them centre of attention. Purple lilac at outer corners of eye blended into socket. Pale mauve highlighter below brow bone and centre of lids. Blue eye liner on top lid very close to eyelashes. Blue pencil under eye – also extremely close to lash line. Very generous with mascara on top and bottom, and brows pencilled quite heavily. Because eyes are quite heavily made up and lips are good and generous, lipstick is a good strong colour.

Photographs by Vince Loden.

foundation stage stay where we have put it. Without it, cream- or oil-based products will shift and smear.

The final effect of a water-based matt foundation, too, is improved by a light veil of powder. If you have chosen a matt finish, it is because you want to conceal spots or to counteract oiliness. In both cases, an extra fluff-on of powder will do nothing but good.

Nowadays, almost all powders are translucent – that is, very light in texture and only slightly tinted. They are a vast improvement on the old-fashioned heavy and strongly-coloured varieties. Tints are now so fragile that most manufacturers make only three shades: extremely light, a honeyish sort of beige and ever-so-slightly tan. So small is the difference that almost all of us can use any of them. The palest *might* show up on an exceptionally dark skin, and black-skinned women must be certain either to pick the darkest or to find one that is absolutely colourless. Otherwise, the choice of shade presents no problem; and 'medium' will do for almost everybody.

Your powder is not meant to add colour. It permits the colour you have already applied to show through. It preserves it. And it provides an underlay for the colour you will add later with blushers, shaders and highlighters.

Translucent powder comes loose in boxes, or compressed into cakes in compacts. I prefer the loose for making up at home, when I am in complete control of the situation, and the compressed for touching up when I am away from my own dressing-table.

Powder boxes and compacts often contain thin foam-rubber pads. These are perfectly adequate for adding a little compressed powder in a hurry, but loose powder should really be applied with a puffier sort of puff. I find double-sided velour the best – easy to handle and easy to wash. Romantic-looking, feminine swans' down puffs are lovely and very efficient; the problem with them, though, is that they cannot be washed. Practical, if not very pretty, are small squares of clean, soft old towelling.

Many people use cotton wool on the theory that it is hygienic: after powdering with it once or twice, you throw it away. I, however, am chary of cotton wool, and never use it on my own face or anyone else's *unless it is dampened*, as when I apply tonic. Obviously, it has to be dry for powder, and that can be dangerous. When dry, it is likely to shed little strands that may catch in the down of your face or, even worse, stray into your eyes.

Applying powder

Pat your powder very, very lightly over your entire face – your forehead, cheeks, chin, throat, lobes, eyelids – wherever you have used foundation. Flip-flop it on. Don't grind or rub it in. Wherever you have wrinkles, especially under your eyes, keep the quantity down to a minimum. Powder, like foundation, will clog and make wrinkles more, rather than less, conspicuous.

Now take a largish soft brush – a make-up brush made especially for the purpose, a baby's hairbrush, an old shaving brush you've pinched from your husband – and gently flick it over every fraction of an inch that you have powdered, to remove any excess. If you have facial down, be careful to brush in the direction the hair grows, just as you did when you put on your foundation.

One last step will accomplish two things: make the finish look a little less matt, should you prefer it that way; and extend the life of your make-up.

Dampen a clean sponge, precisely as you dampened it for applying your foundation, and gently *press* – not rub or stroke – bit by bit over your entire face. Press, lift and move on to the next section. You can also do this by dampening a sheet of cleansing tissue, laying it over your face and letting it cling for a

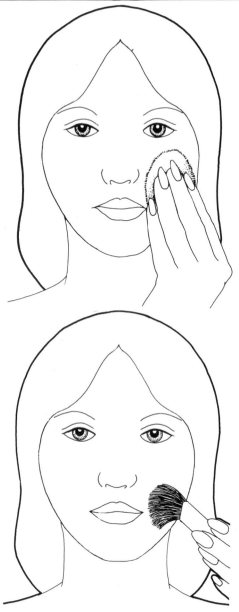

moment; or with a fine spray of Evian water, which you can buy in aerosol containers.

I would advise women with exceptionally oily skin to use this dampening trick, then powder again, dampen once more and finish off with a last dusting of powder. You will be astonished at how long your make-up lasts.

7. Make-up 3: eyes, brows and mouth

Dazzling eyes . . . or dreamy . . . or smouldering. A pensive mouth . . . or sensitive . . . or sexy. Your eyes and your mouth are always sending messages, the signals of your personality. Make-up helps express these messages clearly. It can do more. It can subdue them or heighten them. It can make your eyes look larger or smaller. It can transform their shape.

Whatever illusion you would like, it is at your fingertips: eyes and mouth are immensely responsive to cosmetics. Everything depends upon the proper application of dark and light – shading and highlighting, as always – combined with the clever use of colour.

You create your illusion in a logical step-by-step order:

1.   Shape, shadow and highlight your eyes.

2.   Pencil your brows. They are, in effect, what a picture-frame is to a canvas, so it's only sensible to paint your picture first.

3.   Add the final accent with mascara and, perhaps, false lashes.

4.   Make up your mouth.

There are two good reasons for saving your mouth for last. Your eyes take a lot more doing than your lips. You may work with a fairly elaborate palette. Once you have established the colour and intensity of your eyes, you have the key for how to treat your lips. The tones must never clash, although either eyes or mouth may be pale and the other dark. Even if you should want one to be more highly dramatized than the other, the degree of difference should be carefully modulated.

The second reason: if you put your lipstick on first, you stand a very good chance of smudging it while you're fiddling with your eyes.

A good light is vital. The total impact is the sum of many tiny details. Near-misses on eyes or mouth can be calamities. If your eyesight is at all troublesome, it is a great help – indeed, a necessity – to use a magnifying mirror.

You will, of course, long before you start to make up, have trimmed your eyebrows (Chapter 11), so that their shape is in the correct relationship to your eyes. After proper trimming, you will have given yourself a clearly delineated open space above each eye.

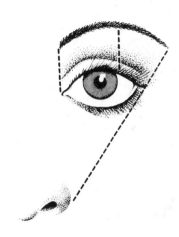

This extends from the *inner* corner to the line slanting upwards from the *outer* corner to the *end* of your brow; and from the *rim* of the *top* lid to the *bottom* edge of your brow. A lovely big area in which to work!

Now ask yourself: 'How best can I make use of this space? What do I want to play down? What do I want to emphasize?' The answers depend upon the size and shape of your eyes; how far apart they are; how deep-set; the sort of lids; bags or shadows, if any.

Are you wondering why I left out the words, 'colour of eyes'? This is not an oversight. You have probably had it drummed into you that the colour of your iris, and that alone, dictates the colour of your eyeshadow. Not so! Unless your eyes are a devastating hue – magnificent blue or violet, arrestingly emerald (in which case you will want to capitalize on them) – you choose your shadow to complement your clothing. Eye make-up is an essential part of your total scheme. It is an accessory. It is not a declaration on its own.

That doesn't translate into 'Bright green dress equals bright green eyes.' If you like bright green and if you can get away with it (taking everything from your skin to your hair to your age to your eyes themselves into consideration), there is no reason why you shouldn't wear it. On the other hand, there is no good reason why you should. Most of us would be better off with a sludgy, rather than a vivid, green, or with a brown, or a mixture of the two, especially by day.

You are coordinating, not matching. A soft mauve on your eyes, perhaps, with a purple dress; deep grey with a red sweater; russet with a brown blouse.

As you grow more adventurous, you will want a selection of varying eyeshadow colours on hand. But don't go mad. Buy one or two to start with, and gradually enlarge your eye wardrobe. It need never be enormous. If you have one black and one white shadow,

for instance, you also have, with blending, every tone of grey.

No matter what colour you choose, you do not cover the entire area with it in the same intensity. The shape, the size and the setting of your eyes (see diagrams, pp. 79–88) will determine where the weight of the colour should lie, where to create shadows with a darker shade, where to highlight.

In general, you put the stronger (or strongest) of the two or more shades on the lids themselves. The exact position for its greatest density shifts for different problems. Lighter tones are blended gradually and subtly upwards and outwards, with no hard edges showing. Highlighters – again, well blended into the neighbouring colour – go either in the centre of the lid, or up high, under or near the browbone.

A little dark shadow is almost always more effective than a lot of light. You may think, 'I can't go wrong with a pale blue.' But you won't always go right either. Pale shadows, without the help of darker ones, can be just plain namby-pamby.

Fashions in eye make-up keep changing, and nothing dates a woman more than clinging stubbornly to an outmoded eye-style.

Eyes these days are 'soft' and will probably stay soft for a long time, because the look is flattering to all ages. Almost every woman now swirls a tiny touch of her lid-colour down under the lower lashes at the outer corner. (A very little. Too much is grotesque.) Almost no one any more wears a harsh, stark line of eyeliner. Women who use eyeliner usually smudge it to produce a hazy edge. Or they dot it with a very fine brush in between the lower lashes, and sometimes add a second line of infinitesimally tiny dots just beneath (almost touching) the first.

False-eyelash fashions have changed too – and all for the good. The heavy, spiky, overbearing picket-fences that were so popular a few years ago have, thank heavens, gone into hiding. False lashes today are, for the most part, simply a natural-looking improvement on your own. With mascara now so excellent and varied, many women have scrapped false lashes entirely. But keep your eyes open: they may be back.

The message about mascara for *everyone* is *wear it*. There is no eye-shape, no eye-type which doesn't benefit from it. Every once in a great, great while I meet a girl whose lashes are perfect – long, sweeping, thick, beautifully coloured. Mascara can do for the rest of us what nature did for her.

May I make a plea to older women? Don't be afraid of eye make-up. In particular, don't be timid about using it *under* your eyes. Somewhere, somehow, the notion has spread that it is ageing to do so. Quite the reverse. A discreet touch of mascara on the lower lids, a faint blur of colour at the outer edges beneath them – both create gentling shadows which help conceal wrinkles and bags.

Selecting and applying your shadow

Once upon a time, cream-shadows were *the* shadows. They are rapidly losing popularity in favour of shadow-pencils and compressed-powder shadows. I wouldn't touch old-style creams with a barge-pole, and I advise you to steer clear of them. They are hard to control; they smear; they clog in wrinkles and exaggerate them.

If you like the feel of something creamy on your lids (some women find compressed powder over-dry), then go for a comparatively new product that looks like a cream and feels like a cream, but acts more like a powder, or for a powder marked 'water proof', which contains emollients. Better still, use shadow-pencils. They are firmer in texture than creams and are, therefore, easier to apply and less likely to clog in

wrinkles. They are also easier to apply than powder shadows, though not quite so satisfying.

Powders come in an enormous variety of subtle shades. They last extremely well, and they are endlessly flexible. I make up at least 1500 pairs of eyes a year, and I never cease to be delighted by the tricks I can play with a combination of powder shadows and pencils.

Pencils

Pencils, like powders, go on over lids which have already been lightly covered with foundation and translucent face-powder. No, that doesn't break the *powder over powder* and *cream over cream* rule. Shadow-pencils are creamy enough to blend smoothly over the powdered foundation.

Pencils come in two shapes – squat and broad, or long and slim like eyebrow pencils. The colour range is good, and you should have no trouble finding what you want. Don't let the fact that they are sometimes labelled 'kohl' pencils confuse you. Their content is in no way related to the black-soot kohl with which ancient Egyptians outlined their eyes. (Did you know, by the way, that this was not for glamour, but to stave off nasty disease-carrying little insects that cling to the eyes in some hot climates?) The squat pencils, because their points are large – like kiddies' crayons – are a little more practical for shadowing, but the slim ones also do the job perfectly well.

You use them as you would a soft drawing pencil, working from the inner corner outwards, adding a bit of colour with each stroke, and gently smudging one tone into the next with a finger, an applicator or a brush. Some women dust a light film of translucent face powder over pencil-shadow, both to set it, and to avoid a shiny look.

Should you want to put a line of colour inside your lower lids (this is fabulous at night), either a slim or a squat pencil will work. The line can subtly echo the dominant colour above, exactly match it or be very bold – bright blue, for instance, with mauve shadow, green with grey. The line may be applied either when you have finished shadowing and before your mascara, or after your mascara, as you choose. (The same holds true for the smudge of eyeliner or those tiny dots I mentioned between the lower lashes. Either before or after the mascara.)

Pencils go blunt rather quickly. Some manufacturers sell little sharpeners to fit their own brands. For slim pencils, you can use the kind of small hand sharpener you buy in stationers. But keep it exclusively for lip and brow pencils; never let ordinary writing pencils anywhere near it. Alternatively, use a sharp knife and finish off with an emery board. Put the pencil in the fridge first; that makes it easier to sharpen.

Shadow powders

You can buy these one colour at a time packed individually in miniature compacts; made up in sets of several different colours, or in sets containing the same colour in two or three shades, from fairly dark to highlighting pale. Such sets almost always include a short wand with a foam-rubber applicator at one end and a brush at the other – sometimes with brushes at both ends, sometimes with only foam-rubbers.

These are adequate enough little tools while they last, which is seldom long enough. They tend to snap in two, or to lose an end, long before the shadows they came with are finished. I find them useful only for a fairly quick light dusting of colour when the powder is dry.

But you will never know what powder shadow can achieve – and how well you can master it – unless you apply it *wet*. It is, after all, compressed powder dust. When you rub the surface with an applicator or a brush, tiny particles flake

off and float about. These are likely to settle anywhere except where you want them – on the wrong part of your eyes, on your cheeks, on your temples.

Treat your cake of powder as though it were a cake of watercolour paint. To paint accurately, as I have said, you need a brush with a fairly long handle, which provides balance and control.

At first, you may find it easier to blend with an applicator than with a brush. You can buy extra applicators, usually in packets of two or three, very cheaply. So you needn't fret if they break or wear out quickly. (Some women use neither brushes nor applicators, but cotton swabs instead. Sensible – if not ideal.)

Once you have learned to use a brush, you will wonder how on earth you ever got along without one (although you may still want to finish off with an applicator). A brush gives you a satin-smooth surface. A brush is absolutely precise, making it possible to deal with the tiniest corner accurately, to paint in a finicky detail.

You can use the same brush for whatever number of shades you apply, so long as you rinse it in clean water and wipe off with a tissue any traces of a dark tone before moving on to a light one. To be on the safe side, use a second brush (or the opposite end of a wand with two brushes) for your highlighter.

So – here is how to apply your powder shadow. Dip your brush (or applicator) into a little pot of water. You need no more than a fraction of an inch of water. Then stroke the brush once or twice over the darkest colour you intend to use. First, try a little on the back of your hand to be sure that the consistency is right. It should smooth on easily and remain where you have placed it – not run off in streaks. Put a little more on your brush if the initial try seems too thin. But go cautiously. Better to be too light on the first go than too dark. It is always easier to add than to subtract.

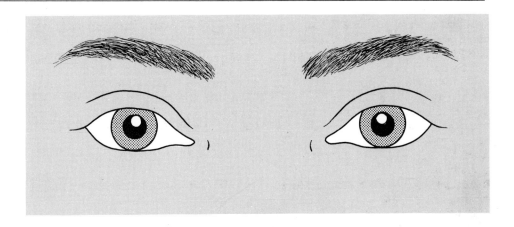

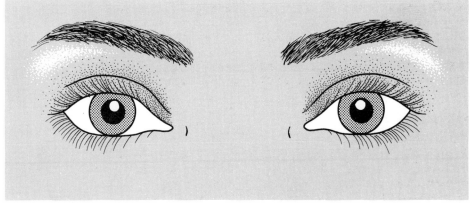

*normal or
average eyes*

Starting from the inner corner, cover as much of your lid as your eye-shape demands. Rinse your brush or clean your applicator, and then, with your second tone, shade off gradually as you near the socket and the outer edges. Do the same with the other lid. Then, little by little, work in the lighter tones where you need them. Finish with your highlighter.

That's all there is to it.

The diagrams which follow show you how to handle your particular eye-shape or eye-problem.

Normal or average eyes

Eyes which are well-set, well-shaped, with a wide open space above them and in good proportion to the rest of your face, are a joy to behold and a joy to possess. You merely take advantage of your God-given assets. You may want to make your eyes look a little larger (most women do), but that presents no problem. It is a simple matter of using a fairly pale shadow on the lid and of highlighting strategically.

Almost anything goes with eyes like these, and it is a great pity not to make them up attractively. Don't get boring; don't always put the same shades in the same places. Play games with the positioning of colours and highlights. Experiment with new fashion notions. You can put your shadow on all over the lid in the normal way, gradually growing lighter as you move from the inner

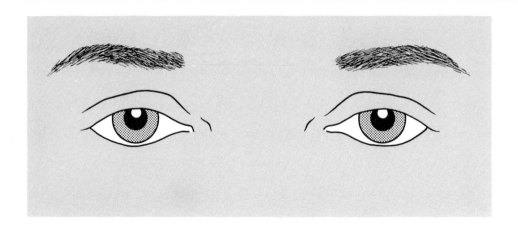

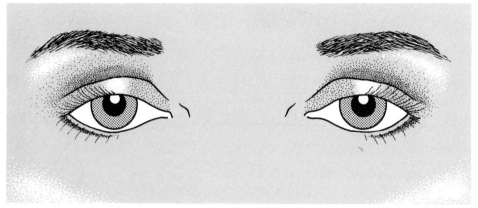

small eyes

corner outwards and upwards. You can be audacious, and use three different shades moving outwards from the *lightest* to the *darkest*. You can highlight down the centre of the lid, or high above near the browbone – or both.

You can put a tinge of a toning colour directly under the eyebrow, a gimmick most eyes cannot get away with. You need have no fear of a vivid pencil-line inside the lower rim, and you can be generous with mascara or false lashes.

Small eyes

To make small eyes look larger, you emphasize their natural shape, unless that, too, needs to be corrected. (See pp.

84–85.) You must use to advantage all the space that is available above them. You may be able to provide yourself with a little extra space by slightly trimming your eyebrows from underneath (see Chapter 11).

Use a fairly light colour over the entire lid. Put a darker shade along the socket line, and then apply another light one as you near your browbone. Thus, you create a three-dimensional effect which is enlarging. White and grey will achieve this more strikingly than a combination of pale and dark of any other colour.

Highlight generously in the centre of the lid. For evening, put a tiny dot of frosted shadow in the centre – *not* blended, for once, simply blobbed on.

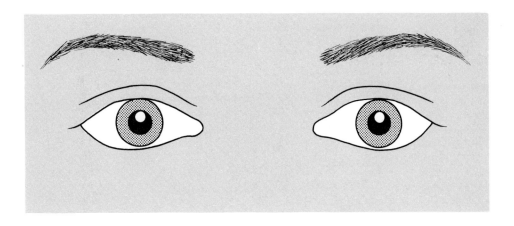

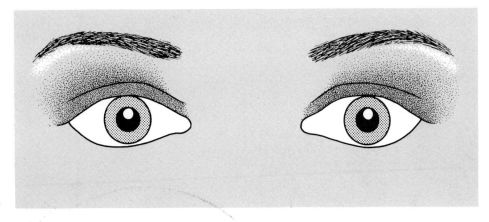

large eyes

You can, with caution, use a subtly pearlized shadow in the daytime, so long as it's not glittery.

You must avoid a stark outline. This simply declares, 'See how small my eyes are!' But do put a smudge of your darkest colour under the bottom lashes, to widen the eye, to 'open' it. Bring it from the outside corner to about the middle of the eye. You can open your eye further ('drop' it, is the word we use in the profession) by leaving a miniscule gap – no shadow at all – between your lower rim and your colour-smudge.

A pencil-line of a very light colour inside the rim is another good enlarging trick. A blusher on the browbone and a highlighter on the cheekbone will also help. So will a half-pair of fine false lashes, top and bottom, with the emphasis at the outer corners, unless your eyes are slitty (see p. 85), as well as small.

Large eyes

Well, lucky old you! You can, like women with normal eyes, play almost any trick that strikes your fancy. On the other hand, you can get away with almost no shadow at all, but lots and lots of mascara.

Large eyes present problems only if they protrude (see p. 82) or if they are hugely out of proportion to a very small face. If yours seem over-large, and you

81

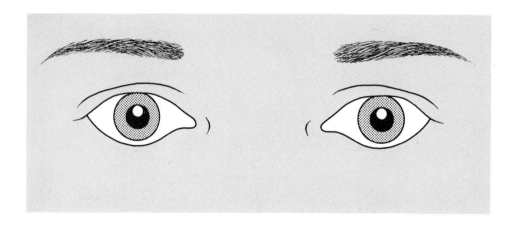

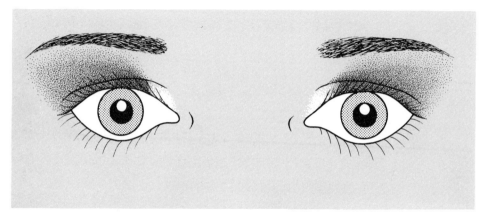

protruding eyes

would rather they didn't dominate all else, use dark and subtle colours rather than bright, light or frosted ones on your lids. Apply them so that you get a soft, smoky edge near the lashes. If the space above the eye is extraordinarily large, bring the shadow up high, to avoid a blank look.

Use only a touch of highlighter or light shadow near the brows to help the shape, if necessary.

Your eyebrows must never be too thin (see Chapter 11), and they must be carefully arched to enclose the entire area, and not to open it wider than need be.

Protruding eyes

The eyes themselves are often large, and the lids, large and bulging. This is not an easy challenge. You must never use light colours, bright colours or frosted shadows. Smudge on a dark, strong shadow close to the lashes and blend it gradually upwards and outwards, reducing the intensity only very, very slightly. You want to achieve a long, more or less triangular shape, with the apex at the inner corner, and the broadest part at the browbone.

Since you are trying to overcome the natural highlights on the lids, you will *never add* highlights. You can, however, use a touch of highlighter at the apex of your triangle in the inner corner. Be

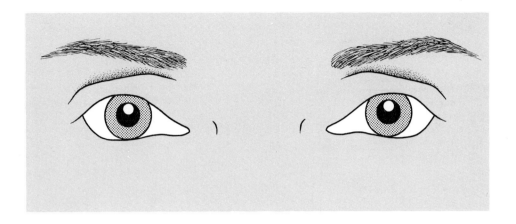

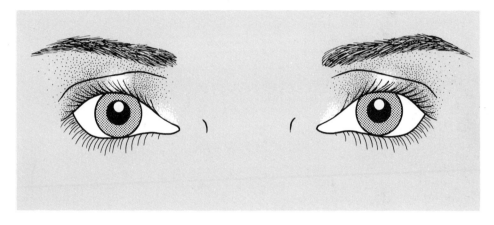

deep-set eyes

generous with mascara. You might also consider a pair of fine false lashes.

Small protruding eyes are, if anything, harder to deal with than large ones. To reduce the bulginess of the lids, you must use dark shadows, as above. This, alas, also reduces the eye-size. If possible, trim your eyebrows from underneath to give a little extra space (see Chapter 11). You cannot highlight the centre of the lids, as with ordinary small eyes. You can, however, use a touch of highlighter in the inner corners, and another touch close to the cheekbones. Otherwise, try to 'open' your eyes with the tricks I have described under *small eyes*.

Deep-set eyes

These are difficult to change, but not impossible. Your quarrel is with your bone structure. Your browbones are prominent and cast heavy shadows over your eyes, making them look stern. Your cheekbones are also likely to be strong. So you must not highlight either.

On the other hand, you must take pains to lighten your lids. With careful shading of a light, sludgy colour you can soften the deep natural shadow in the socket. Use your colour over the entire area between your lashes and your browbone, gradually lightening it as you move upwards. With great care, you can actually take it *onto* the browbone.

83

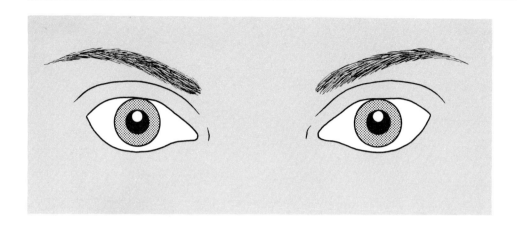

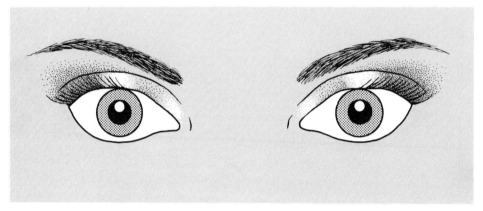

round eyes

Highlight the centre of your lids and, if your eyes are extremely deep-set, also put a little highlighter far into the inner corners, towards the nose. A set of fine false lashes will make your eyes look gentler.

There is a second and a totally different approach to deep-set eyes. Don't try to counteract them. Instead, take advantage of their natural drama. This, however, is only for evening. And only if you have a vivid personality, and if you are neither too young nor too old.

Use an extremely dark shadow – navy blue, deep green – over the entire lid, all the way up to the browbone. Swirl it around along the outer edge below the lower lid. Then dot highlighter onto the centre of the lid.

You will look a typical 1930s, smouldering sex pot. Very exciting; rather dangerous for those who don't intend to tempt.

Round eyes

Round eyes can be either small or large. To elongate them, and counteract the startled look, apply your shadow rather heavily at the outer corners, and blend it upwards and outwards towards the brow. You must avoid the temptation to follow the eye's natural shape. Everything you do is aimed at adding length and reducing width. Highlight the centre and the inner corners of your lids. Avoid shadow beneath the lower lids. This 'drops' the eye and will make it look even rounder.

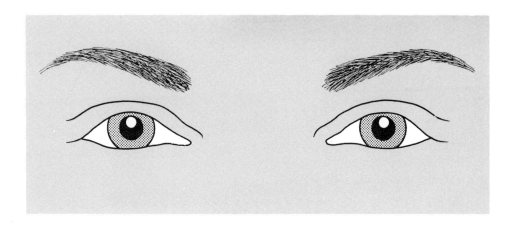

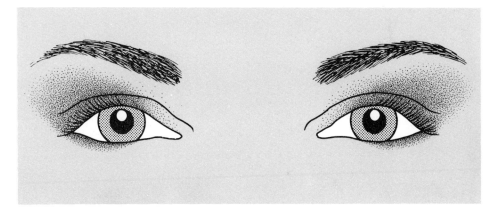

almond eyes

If you use a filament mascara, make your top lashes look as long as possible at the outer corners. Induce them to stretch towards your temples. Alternatively, fix a half-pair of false lashes to the top lids only, with the sweep towards the outer corners. Accentuate the illusion of length with highlighter above the outer corners, near the cheekbones, and with a small amount of blusher high on the cheek.

Be certain not to trim your eyebrows (see Chapter 11) into a half-moon shape. You should have a long, angular sweep – a bird's-wing effect. You will have extended your shadow as far out as possible. Extend your brows, as well, to frame the entire shadowed area.

Almond eyes

These tend to be rather long and narrow, with an upward tilt at the outer corners. Most people find them extremely attractive – so long as the slant is not over-exaggerated and the eyes not so narrow as to look like slits. If, however, you loathe your slant, you can overcome it with dark shadow applied quite heavily at the outer corners, both on the lids and under the bottom lashes. You must take great care not to extend the darkness beyond the ends of the eyes. The tricks for 'opening' small eyes will also work for you.

If your eyes are set fairly wide apart, you can also put a touch of dark shadow on the inner corners, near the nose, and

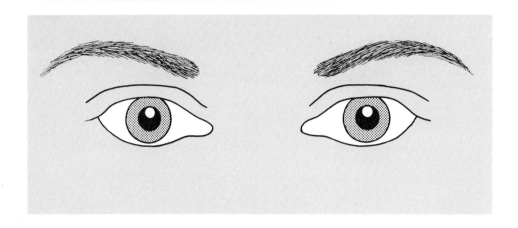

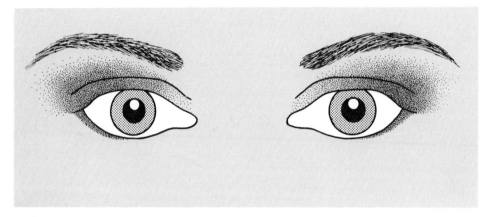

close-set eyes

blend it upwards to balance the upward tilt at the outer corners. This is dangerous if they are close-set; it will only bring them closer together. Finish with a light highlight in the centre of the lids.

If you like your almond shape and want to accentuate it, wear false lashes on the outer corners of the top lids. If you want to counteract the slant, wear fine false lashes with the emphasis in the *centre* on the top, and with the emphasis of the bottom lash *down* at the *outer* corner.

Be careful not to extend the length of your brows if you are trying to diminish the elongated eye-shape.

Close-set eyes

Eyes of any shape or size can be set too close together, leaving only a comparatively small space across the bridge of the nose. Make them up to suit their natural shape, but, to create the illusion of greater space between them, avoid dark shadow at the inner corners. Start with a light shade near the nose and gradually blend in darker tones as you move outwards and upwards. You will probably want to extend your shadow well beyond your eyes. Bring the dark shadow down below the outer corners of the eyes only, and never further in than the centre.

When you trim your eyebrows (see Chapter 11), clear as much space as you

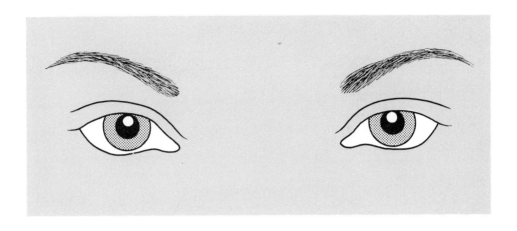

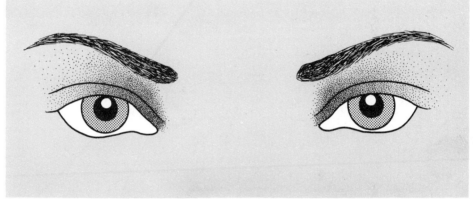

eyes too wide apart

safely can above the nose. But careful! If you trim back too far, the result can be a disconcerting patch of bare skin. It can also make your eyebrows look as if they were sliding off the sides of your face. Extend your brows outwards, to follow the line of your extended shadow.

Eyes too wide apart

As with close-set eyes, these can be of any shape or size. There is too much space between them, which can make the bridge of the nose appear to be extremely broad. You make up your eyes to suit their natural shape and size, but your emphasis is precisely the opposite of that for the woman whose eyes are too close together. Always concentrate the darkness at the inside corners, and gradually blend in your lighter tones towards the outside. If you are certain of soft lighting at night, you can bring a small touch of your dark shade fractionally down onto the sides of the nose-bridge. To bring the shading further down the sides of your nose, use a touch of shaper. Unless your nose is very long, apply a highlighter down the centre. In the daytime, skip the eyeshadow at the bridge, and use only a shader for slimming your nose, and no more than the faintest hint of a highlight down the centre.

Your eyebrows must never be trimmed too far apart at the centre (see Chapter 11). You may, in fact, want to

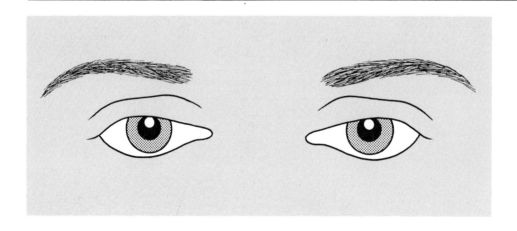

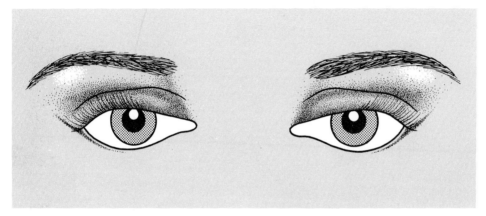

hooded eyes

bring them slightly closer together with your pencil. Never extend them beyond the natural shadow area.

Hooded eyes

Hooded eyes are heavy-lidded. There is actually a little more skin than the eyes need to cover them, and this tends to droop at a downwards angle towards the outer corners. No matter what your eye-shape, if your lids are hooded, you must cheat upwards with everything you do. Use a fairly dark shadow at the inner corners, and blend it upwards – *above* the outer corners, not following the natural edges of the lids.

If your eye-shape permits, dramatize the area high under the brow with colour, and highlight the browbones. Counteract the downward droop by drawing a very fine line (with eyeliner or pencil) from the bottom lid upward.

A half-pair of false lashes will also help you to cheat. Draw a light line from the centre of the top lid straight across to the outer end of the eye, bypassing the little drooping triangle. Attach your lashes along this line, from about the centre of your lid, and make certain that they curl well upward to give the entire eye a lift.

A hint for a quick eye make-up

When you are in a mad rush, with no time to shadow your eyes correctly, your blusher or shader will keep them from looking naked and neglected. With the same broad brush you use on your face, sweep over your lids and on up to your browbones. If you can spare one extra moment, add a whisper of colour to the lids with powder shadow. Models often do this when they are rushing from one assignment to the next. (So do I.)

Eyebrows

You and your tweezers have given your brows the shape you want (see Chapter 11). Now you accentuate with make-up. You can extend the arch slightly in either direction, to help your eye-shape or to narrow or broaden the bridge of your nose. You can fill in a little underneath or above, to correct the proportion of the space between eye and brow.

As with all else, the effect must be natural. An eyebrow drawn in a hard, sharp line makes the entire face look cold and artificial.

The colour of your eyebrow pencil should be a near match to your hair. Obviously, there are exceptions. A redhead would look ludicrous with matching red brows, and a blonde or a woman with white hair would appear to have no brows at all if they stuck to their hair colour. Pencils are normally sold in light, medium and dark brown and in grey and black. (You can also buy gold ones, which look smashing on blondes, flecked over a light brown or medium brown pencil.) Most women get along perfectly well with one of the standard colours. It is sometimes cannier to mix a couple. A reddy brown on its own is too red for almost anyone, even a vivid redhead; tone it down with dark brown. Unrelieved black may prove too stark, no matter how black your hair, especially if your brows are fairly heavy; lighten it with medium brown. Grey alone can look slightly blue on some faces; warm it with dark brown.

Pale blondes, whose brows are so fair as to be almost invisible, may find it difficult to pencil hairs which they can hardly see. It is easier to brush colour onto them – by touch, almost as much as by sight – with a mascara brush which has on it no more than a trace of dry mascara, light or medium brown.

Before you pencil your brows, brush them with a stiff, small brush (an old clean mascara brush will do) to remove any foundation or powder that might have strayed on to them, and to smooth their shape. Working from the nose outward, draw one tiny hairline after another, covering each hair in the direction it naturally grows. If your brows are sparse, thicken them with extra lines between the real hairs.

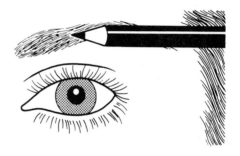

Each stroke is exceedingly fine – no broader than the hairs themselves. You must, therefore, work with a very sharp point. I prefer a flat, chisel-shaped end to a round one. I think it draws a more hairlike hair. Sharpen yours in the first place with a very keen knife, and maintain its edge with a used emery board.

To achieve absolute perfection – little hairs that only God could tell from the real thing – paint them in with a delicately pointed brush moistened with an infinitesimal amount of eyeliner.

Whenever you draw or paint hairs on bare skin – outward towards the temples; inward towards the bridge of your nose; above or below the brow's natural line – you must be especially painstaking about drawing them individually. Otherwise they will look like what they are: phoney extensions.

Mascara

In the old days, almost every girl I knew owned an eyelash curler. They are not quite so popular as they used to be. Thanks to the versatility of modern mascara, many women find they can get along without them; they flick their lashes upward effectively with the mascara itself. But if your lashes are stubbornly straight, you do need a curler.

Only a curler, in any case, will give you a full rolling sweep that lifts your lashes high. This is a lovely look on lovely eyes. If it is the look you want, be sure to use your curler *before* you apply your mascara. Try to do it afterwards, and you'll wind up with a right royal mess – squashed lashes and dark flakes all over the place. Not only that. Because mascara stiffens your lashes, you stand a good chance of breaking them.

You can buy mascara compressed into blocks, which you apply with a brush and water. You can buy it in tubes with built-in swirly round brushes on wands. There are two types of the tube-and-wand variety. One contains tiny filaments which thicken and lengthen your lashes. The second is finer and lighter in weight, and merely colours the lashes without markedly changing their texture.

The blocks are never waterproof. The other two almost always are. The blocks, however, are usually safer than the others for anyone who shows signs of an allergy to mascara.

An urgent note about blocks. I shudder to think of the number of women I have seen wetting their mascara brushes with their own spit. If ever there was a disgusting habit, this is it. Unhygienic to a degree! Mouths carry germs, and there is no easier way to give yourself an eye infection. Dampen your brush in clean water, under the tap or from a little pot or jar on your dressing-table.

You may want to switch the types about. Many women wear lengthening-thickening mascara only in the evening, and a more natural-looking variety during the day. If you are going to swim, if your eyes water in the wind, or, (heaven forbid) if you're a weepy type, you will obviously want one that is waterproof.

As for colours, take your pick from among varying shades of brown, from light to dark; black; grey, and blue. Dark brown and black work well for most women. Blue is good for many. Light brown is only for the fairest of the fair, and even they often need the help of something slightly darker. Grey, I think, is a little wishy-washy.

Anyone can learn to put mascara on skilfully. All it takes is a little practice. No one need ever have lashes clotted into little clumps.

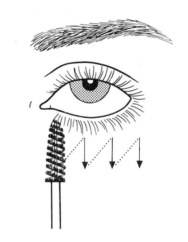

Mascara your bottom lashes first. (If you do the top first, you'll smear them while you're working on the bottom.) Bend your head forward and roll your eyes upward to look into your mirror. Your brush or wand should not be too heavily loaded. Hold the brush *vertically* and, using firm, even, downward strokes, coat your lashes several at a time. Move either from the inside corner out or the outside in, whichever you find easier.

Let them dry, and then, with a clean brush – I always save an old wand-brush for this – carefully separate the lashes. (One manufacturer has recently introduced a wonderful gadget, a mascara wand with a second brush tucked in at the bottom for separating the lashes. I hope the idea catches on.)

Give them a second coat. Separate them again. And coat them a third time if you like. The more layers you apply, the lusher your lashes look – so long as you separate them well each time.

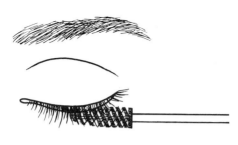

Now to your top lashes. Lean your head well back, and look downward. Hold your brush *horizontally*. Use a wiggly, circular movement, always curving upwards, and cúrling your lashes as you cover them. Be extra careful to do this with your last strokes. Again, work in either direction. Again, separate the lashes when they are dry. Again, use as many coats as you like.

For lashes which are very pale, put a coat on the top surface of the hairs first. Separate, and then proceed as above.

Many women apply only one or two layers to the lower lashes, but as many as four or five on top. You can start with a little in the morning – say, if you're rushing off to work – and add a layer or two whenever you get the chance, so that by the evening your eyes are a knockout. Particularly effective with a filament mascara, which lengthens and thickens a bit more with every application.

If yours are naturally long, don't go berserk. Too much mascara will leave tiny marks on your cheeks. But there is a way round that one too: dust an edging of face-powder on the tips. It will be invisible.

I have heard it said that to be glamorous in bed, you should keep your mascara on. Far be it from me to spoil anyone's fun, but I think it's a mucky habit. Mascara rubs off on pillow-slips, on to your face and on to any other face that happens to be nearby. I personally like to take all my make-up off at night. As I have said before, no one has to climb into bed covered with revolting, greasy gunk.

The cleansers that you use to take everything else off your face will do perfectly well for your eyes. You can buy little pads – they usually are rather oily – made to remove eye make-up. There is also a non-greasy product available, a clear liquid that looks like water, and is very efficient. I myself find liquid paraffin extremely efficient.

False lashes

Will false lashes make your eyes look prettier? Will they help solve a problem? The answer to both may well be 'yes'. But not everyone needs them or wants them. They can, however, as you will have seen from my eye diagrams, often improve the improvements you achieve with your make-up. Sometimes they can do more than the make-up itself.

I am not talking about enormous flappers. These, in my view, are good fun – but for drag artists only. I mean lashes that look as though they belong to real people. They can be thick or fine, short or long, so natural in appearance that even your best friends won't guess. Or deliberately exotic.

As with buying shoes, you must know in advance what you're looking for. If you need black moccasins, you don't settle for stiletto-heeled gold sandals. Do you want fine lashes in a soft shade for daytime wear? Thicker, longer, darker

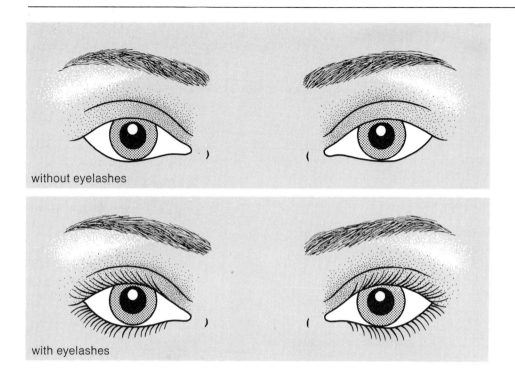

without eyelashes

with eyelashes

ones for evening? Top lashes? Bottom? Both? A colour that matches your own? Or something a little stronger? Sort it out for yourself, and don't let anyone sell you anything that doesn't answer your needs or desires.

A beginner-wearer like a beginner-driver should not be overbold. Lashes that are too extreme might shock your beloved out of his wits. Let your adventurousness grow gradually.

When false lashes first became big business some years ago, we all scorned artificial fibres. They were indeed horrid, and nothing but real hair would do. Things have changed, however. Fibre ones have been perfected to a fine art, and they are a great improvement over the real thing. Natural-hair lashes are prey to the same problems as the hair on your head. They go straight and lank when it is damp or hot, and you have to re-curl them – an awful nuisance. Fibre ones remain exactly as they were when you bought them.

Putting lashes on is a bit finicky, but you'll pick the knack up after a try or two. (I wouldn't have my first attempt on the night of a special date. Get them a few days in advance, and put in some practice.) There are two things to remember:

1. Apply mascara to your own lashes before you glue on your false ones. *Never* mascara the fakes!

2. Lashes are attached to fine strips, which are made in one size only. So you must trim from the strips the length you need to extend along the lid – or that part of it – where you want to wear them. The lashes are attached in tiny groups, and you snip by groups, not by individual hairs, always from the outer end. *Never* try to shorten the hairs themselves; it is impossible to do this accurately.

To measure, take the lashes carefully out of their box with your fingers or a pair of tweezers. Put your head well

these little cut-off bits. They will come in handy when you feel like wearing no more than a few at the outer corners.

With every pair of lashes, you get a small tube of glue. (You can buy extra glue separately.) Squeeze the tiniest droplet on to the back of your hand. Pick up the lashes with the other hand – fingers or tweezers – and pull the base of the strip through the drop of glue. With head and mirror in the same position as before, and holding your elbow very high, set the lashes above and as close to your own lashes as possible.

Either with a fingertip or with the blunt end of your tweezers, first pat the centre down firmly, and then the edges. Stroke along the entire line until the lash adheres – a matter of a moment or two. The glue by then will have lost its whitish colour and be absolutely clear.

Now hold the fakes and your own together with your fingers for a few seconds. The fake ones stick to the mascara on the real, and the two sets intermingle. You may want to smudge a little eyeliner along the base, but, I repeat, *no* mascara on the false ones. It makes them look horrid. It also makes them messy; you'd be tempted to try to clean them, and that's a good way to ruin them.

When you first put your lashes on, especially if you've never worn them before, you will be physically aware of them. It won't be discomfort – merely the feeling of something strange.

Taking them off should be no more uncomfortable than putting them on. Support the skin of your lid with the first or second finger of one hand and, grasping the lashes between the thumb and first finger of the other hand, pull them gently *forward*. Ease them off little by little, starting either from the outer or the inner corner. Never rip them off horizontally along the length. This can be painful, because you would be pulling contrary to the direction in which your own lashes grow.

back and, with your chin high, peer down along your nose into a mirror held close to your face. Both eyes are open, both lids clearly visible.

Lay a strip of lash along the edge of one lid (it will balance there quite safely) to see how much needs to be trimmed away. Do not start at the absolute inner corner of your eye, but anywhere from a quarter to half an inch towards the centre – at the point where your natural lashes begin, or even a little beyond. If you put false ones too near your nose, they will get in the way when you close your eyes, and you will feel a sharp, prickling sensation. This will irritate the eyes; it could make them water, and the lashes might loosen and fall off.

If your eyes are large, you may need to snip nothing away. If your eyes are small, or if you want the lashes along only part of your lid, you will probably have to take off several groups. Play safe. Cut off one group at a time. Measure again. And snip again. Save

When you have removed them, hold the lashes by their hairs – again between thumb and first finger – and, with the first finger of the other hand, strip the glue off the base. And they are ready for the next time. If you put them carefully back into the box between wearings, a good pair of lashes will never need to be cleaned. Even if you wear them every day, they should last for several months.

Semi-permanent false lashes

Salons will attach false lashes to your own, one by one, in a slow, tedious and expensive process. (You can also buy do-it-yourself kits.) With care, these will last from four to six weeks. 'Care' in this case can lead you to a dizzy peak of silliness.

You must never put mascara on them. You must clean around them and try not to touch them. You must be careful not to crumple them. I know one girl who even taught herself to sleep on her back so she wouldn't disturb her lashes.

No matter how hard you try, a few are almost certain to drop off or break off and send you scooting back to the salon to have them replaced between regular renewals.

To my mind, they are simply not worth the trouble. Go in for this, and you could be well on your way to becoming a beauty bore.

Party tricks

There are times when we all want to let the old Eve loose. Christmas. New Year's Eve. A fancy-dress gala. This once, forget the natural look I've been preaching; you are the fairy on the top of the tree. Go all out with your eyes.

Try these.

Strengthen your shadow. Add extra lashes at the outside corners. Put frosted highlighter on your lids. Pencil a line of vivid colour in your lower rims. Use a pearly highlighter on your cheekbones to bring a new glow to your eyes. Or dust a little soft glitter-powder over the centre of your lids. Particles will waft down onto your cheeks – not much, but enough to make you sparkle when the light catches you.

For a bit of delightfully zany bezazz, buy tiny gold or silver stars of miniature sequins and fasten a few with eyelash glue to your lids or your browbones.

But please, please, only at night! And only on festive, irresponsible occasions!

Spectacles and contact lenses

The witty and sometimes wise writer, Dorothy Parker, frequently wore glasses. And the record shows that, despite her famous couplet, she was rarely at a loss for passes. I have yet to meet a girl who ever lost a man because she had a pair of spectacles perched on her nose. If lose him she did, there were always a lot of other better reasons.

Should your sight be poor, I hope you have the common sense to get your eyes checked regularly, and the fashion sense to choose prettifying frames. Not round with a round face, nor broad with a broad face. And the right colour for your hair and skin. Glasses can actually be an asset, not a disadvantage, obscuring bad features and flattering good ones.

More and more girls now wear fairly large frames, to let the world see the entire eye area, attractively made up. More and more, too, have taken to contacts, now that the lenses are so much more pliable and comfortable than they used to be. That decision is between you and your optician. Wearing either, you make up your eyes exactly as everyone else does, with a couple of exceptional *do's* and *don'ts*.

The biggest problem is seeing yourself clearly enough to put the make-up on. If you are short-sighted, a top-quality magnifying mirror is essential. Contact-wearers often make up with their lenses in, so that they can see what

right

wrong

For contact lenses: You must be wary of all make-up with bits and pieces in it. Anything gritty caught inside the lenses can cause agony. So – *no* filaments in your mascara. Powdered shadows *only* if used *wet*. *Nothing* frosted. And *no* lines inside your lower rims: the colour may coat the lenses.

For glasses of normal strength: You can afford to overstate all your eye make-up, not wildly, but enough for it to be seen – not seen through a glass darkly.

For glasses with strong magnification: You must understate. Whatever you put on your eyes appears bigger, heavier and brighter to the viewer than it really is. If your glasses are tremendously strong, you may want to forego shadow altogether and restrict yourself to a little mascara and, possibly, a pair of fine false lashes.

Eye care

Even if you don't wear spectacles – and don't think you need them – you should have your eyes tested once a year. You may be straining them without realizing it.

Your eyes and the skin around them are extremely sensitive. Never pull or stretch the skin, especially beneath the eyes. Follow the massage routine, moving your fingers delicately, when you put eye make-up on, and when you take it off.

There is nothing better for tired eyes than rest and sleep. Eyedrops will brighten your eyes and help ease the discomfort and smarting that comes from overwork, or from spending too much time in a smoky room, a cold wind or glaring sunshine. You can't go wrong with the simple straightforward formulas that chemists sell.

But please stay away from blue drops, except in the direst circumstances. They

they are doing. I have known a few ingenious wearers of spectacles who pull them down to the ends of their noses and manage to peer through them while they do their eyes.

Opticians have recently come to the rescue with their own species of ingenuity – spectacles with lenses that flip up separately, so that you can look at yourself with one eye while you make up the other. These are so new on the market that you may have trouble finding them. They're worth the search.

will, admittedly, clear up bloodshot eyes quickly. They contract the tiny veins which show red on the surface of the eyeball and – hey presto – the veins become invisible. Great! But who are you to decide the size of your veins? Think about it. The manufacturers themselves warn against using blue drops too frequently.

Eye-washes, either from an eyecup or on pads of cotton wool, are soothing. I would stick with the commercial ones; they are guaranteed antiseptic. You can't feel quite so sure about any mixture you concoct at home. If you save a few pennies you run a big risk.

Eye-pads work wonders for red, tired or swollen eyes. Again, I believe in commercial ones, and for the same reasons. There are a couple of home substitutes, however, which are perfectly safe. A couple of wads of cotton wool soaked in cold water do an amazing amount of good. Even better are teabags, steeped, then chilled in the fridge. Thin slices of cucumber are cooling and slightly astringent. So are thin slices of potato.

Dark glasses will, of course, conceal redness or swelling. They also provide a bit of protection against the effects of smoke, wind and sun. But don't hide behind them. They are meant to be an aid, not an escape-route from reality.

If your eyes are irritated or sore, take care, take care. You could have a slight infection. Forget eye make-up for a day or so. Rest them and bathe them. And see your doctor.

Under no circumstances ever borrow anyone else's brushes or applicators. And never lend yours. Eye infections are easily transferred.

Mouth make-up

Up to a point, you must live with the mouth that nature bestowed upon you. John Galsworthy, author of *The Forsyte Saga*, once wrote, 'One's eyes are what

one is, one's mouth what one becomes.' He was right. Your personality does determine your mouth's expression. But your make-up can make a remarkable difference to its shape. Which in turn can improve its expression.

You will remember that your colour choice depends upon what you have already put on your eyes, and that that has been decided by what you intend to wear. Unless, as I have said, you want one or the other to play the leading role, the rule in general is vivid eyes, vivid mouth; pale eyes, pale mouth.

You should own at least two fairly dark lipstick pencils, one rather russety, the other brighter and redder (a reddish brown eyebrow pencil will do); a lip-brush and as many lipstick colours as your heart desires and your purse permits. You can, of course, always mix a couple of colours to enlarge your range.

The pencils must have good sharp points – round, not wedge-shaped. As for eye pencils, use a little sharpener or a sharp knife, and smooth with an old emery board.

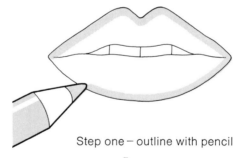

Step one – outline with pencil

First, outline the edges of your lips with your pencil, always darker than your lipstick and, obviously, of a colour that tones. Draw a good, firm, clear line. The better you do this, the better your mouth will look and the less chance there will be of your lipstick 'bleeding'. Give yourself a well-drawn outline in the morning, and for the rest of the day all you are likely to have to do is touch up with your lipstick without worrying

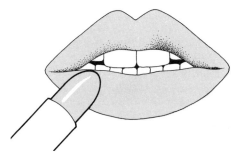

Step two – fill in with lipstick

or brush

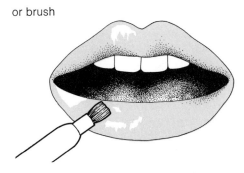

about the shape. It doesn't matter at all whether you work from the cupid's bow to the corners or the other way round.

Step two is to follow the outline with your lipstick, and then fill in, covering well, going back and forth over the mouth. You can do this directly with the stick, but you will do it far more expertly with a brush. A pointed filbert shape is best; a flat end will do, so long as you can re-trace your outline accurately, to assure a clean edge. The brush also gives you a smoother finish. One more thing: it is economical. Long after your lipstick has been worn down too far to be usable, you can scoop out what remains with your brush.

You need own only one brush. A quick wipe with cleansing tissue removes any colour that clings and leaves it ready for another shade.

Mouths are easy, really. So little effort for such fabulous effects. Even corrections are not very difficult. As with all else, the lighter and brighter the colour,

the larger it appears. To reduce a big mouth, use subdued shades and harden your heart against frosted, glossy or iridescent products. To enlarge a tiny mouth, the opposite. If one lip is markedly bigger than the other – a pendulous lower, say, and a thin top – even them up with a slightly lighter shade on the small, and a darker on the large. When one lip is naturally lighter in pigmentation than the other (this is frequently the case with black-skinned women), use a light and a dark shade of the same colour to make them match.

You can change both shape and size with your outline pencil. You can tilt up the corners of a droopy mouth. You can, within limits, straighten a slanting mouth. But before you do anything drastic, be sure you're right. (Remember my stunning friend with the big broad grin? She would lose half her charm if her mouth were half the size.)

Needless to say, you can't cheat too much. You can go only a fraction outside or inside your own lip-edges; any more becomes conspicuous. A false line outside the real one will betray itself most obviously at the cupid's bow, where, because the lip-muscle is strong, there is a clearly defined plane. If you bring the line up too high, it may collide with the natural highlight on this plane, and distort rather than improve.

Use a brown pencil to change your outline, unless you plan to wear a very dark lipstick. In that case, you will need a pencil with more red in it.

Women with dry or wrinkly mouths should avoid frosted lipsticks, because they can be drying, and light colours, because they show up the wrinkles. Opt instead for something rather dark and rich. In extremes of hot or cold, when your lips may be exceptionally dry, remember that your lipstick provides protection as well as beauty; always wear it. If your lips are chapped, use one of the sticks especially made to meet the problem – covering but not colouring.

Women who have trouble keeping lip-stick on, or whose lipstick smears, should avoid glossy products entirely. Whatever lipstick you wear, it will stay put longer if you blot it by pressing your lips against a piece of cleansing tissue. Even better: before you apply your lip-stick, put a tiny amount of foundation on your mouth. Blot the lipstick. Powder very lightly. Apply a second layer of lipstick. (No, you are not blend-ing; you are covering.) Then blot again.

If you are an impossible lipstick-wearer – if it comes off on your teeth or on the rim of your cocktail glass – then don't make yourself miserable. Avoid bright colours or do without lipstick entirely. Outline your lips with a russety pencil and fill in with a clear, colourless lip-gloss.

This brings me to the definition of 'lip-gloss'. There is one type of product by that name which is excellent. There is a second which is very difficult to handle. Further to confound confusion, they are both sometimes known as 'lip-shine'.

The ones I hesitate to recommend come packed in tubes and contain wands with foam-rubber applicators. They are sometimes coloured; they can be runny, sloppy or smeary.

The ones I like are packaged in little pots. They are the consistency of jam and incredibly easy to use. Sometimes they are ever so slightly tinted – say, to a natural skin colour. Usually they are entirely colourless and will give your lips shine only. Many women put them on over regular lipsticks to add a touch of sheen.

Tooth care

You can glorify your mouth so that it's irresistible. Kissable lips – you've got them! But there is not much point in bothering if, when you smile, you reveal a set of dirty, spotted teeth. When dentists counsel you to clean them at least twice a day, their good advice is meant for looks as well as health. Be sure you have two tooth brushes, so you can alternate them. And never neglect the six-monthly dental check-up: stop the rot before it starts.

Don't break your heart if a tooth or two is a wee bit out of line. This can be charming, and, in an odd way, express the quintessential you.

Really wretched teeth, however – huge fangs, hideous buck-like pro-trusions – may send you hot-footing off to find out about cosmetic dentistry. This is costly, uncomfortable and time-consuming. But it can work miracles. You are aware by now that I don't exactly go overboard for plastic surgery. Cosmetic dentistry is rather different. A set of crowns (or caps) can transform your appearance – and your state of mind. Once done, if they are done right, they last a lifetime.

I have known women who have given up their new winter wardrobes or their summer holidays and spent the money on their teeth instead. I have yet to meet one who regretted it.

Days of disaster

No one we know, of course, ever has a hangover, or a horrid squabble that leaves her in tears. But in case you should hear of anyone who does have traumas or dramas, you might want to pass along a hint or two.

If you cry when you're wearing make-up, there is usually no way out but to mop it up, take it off and start all over again. There you are, with swollen eyes and a pink nose. You're lucky if you're at home, where you can lie down for a quarter of an hour or so with a couple of pads on your tortured lids. Home or away, put drops in your eyes.

Then to repairs. Apply your regular foundation and, for pink nose and eyes (you would do this if you had a cold, too) apply a second layer of a slightly heavier foundation. If they are vividly red, use a mint foundation (p. 69) under your regular one.

Treat swollen eyes as you would heavy-lidded eyes (p. 88). Avoid russety shadows – anything with even the slightest tinge of red – and use dark blues or greys. Treat the temporary bags under your eyes as though they were permanent ones (p. 72). Wear a little more mascara than you usually do. Put a darkish line of colour inside your lower rims to make them look less bloodshot.

If, after all that, the ravages still show, pop on a pair of tinted glasses, smile – and hope that people are too polite to notice.

Whether others notice or not, you can feel better and actually look better, by being extra nice to yourself. Trot out your gladdest rags, and don't worry that they will have to go to the cleaner sooner than you'd planned. Be generous with your most fabulous perfume. If you always take saccharine in your coffee, take sugar for once, and blow the diet!

As for hangovers, well, the best thing to do about them is not to get them. No, I don't mean, 'Never let liquor sully your lips.' But if you know that you are in for an evening with more than a ripple of tipple, stoke up in advance with something bulky like bread and butter to help absorb the alcohol, and with something fatty like milk or chocolate to help prevent it from entering your system. When you get home, drink a glass or two of water – tap or mineral – to counteract the dehydration.

You did all that? And it's tomorrow morning? And you still feel wonky? Have a glass of hot water with lots of lemon and plenty of honey. You need blood-sugar, and honey (thanks to all those clever little bees who pre-digest the sugar) gives it to you quickly. Even if you think you can't bear it, eat a slice of toast. Take a glucose tablet or two and, during the course of the day, drink as many glasses of water or fruit juice as you can manage.

Cover your pallor with slightly rosier make-up than usual. Treat your eyes as above if they are swollen or be-bagged. And try to take life easy. This is the day for a taxi if you have an urgent appointment. It may mean no lunch tomorrow, which can't do your figure any harm. It may mean putting off the new pair of shoes you have been saving for. It's worth it. Anything is, so long as you don't have to fight the crowds on the buses or the underground when you are feeling blooming miserable.

8. Make-up 4: the essentials – cosmetics and tools

At home

The ideal, of course, is to have your own dressing-table, with plenty of surface, lots of drawer space and a clear, bright balanced light. But many households are far too crowded to permit the luxury of that much personal privileged space. Mum and dad share the only bedroom chest-of-drawers. The best light and the best mirror are in the bathroom, with the entire family (or a covey of flatmates) clamouring to get in.

I can only say that whomever you have to jostle to get to the mirror, you must organize all your make-up and tools so that you can put your hands on *what* you want *when* you want it.

If you do make up in the bathroom, and there is no room for your essentials there – thanks to the rest of the clan's toothpaste, shampoos, razors and so on – then set out the things you regularly use on a tray, which you keep on top of the chest-of-drawers, or in a large plastic box tucked into a convenient drawer. Available and portable. Ready and waiting for when it's your turn for the mirror.

Many women, in any case, keep their cleansing creams or lotions in the bathroom, because they like to remove their make-up just before they bathe. Most – and I am among them – prefer to keep everything in the bedroom.

Divide your make-up into two sections: the things you need daily immediately to hand; the things you use rarely – the turquoise eyeshadow you wear only with one turquoise evening dress, the bronze foundation you take only on beach holidays – out of the way in a separate plastic box or bag. (I say 'plastic', by the way, because it is so easy to wash; far better than wooden, cardboard or metal boxes.) Don't clutter up or tangle your 'regulars' with your 'once-in-a-whiles'.

Arrange your cosmetics by categories, so that even when you are groping sleepily first thing in the morning, you will know that your foundations, say, are on the right-hand side of the top drawer, your face powder beside them and your eyeshadows, mascara and so on, on the left-hand side. It's a good idea, and it looks attractive, too, to stand all your pencils, brushes and applicators up in a bunch in a decorative little vase or mug.

What, then, are the things you are most likely to need?

Cosmetics

1. *Foundations.*
   Preferably two, one for day, one for evening
   Definitely two, one lighter, one darker, if you need them for face-shaping
   A third, slightly heavier, for covering spots or blemishes
   A medicated, if you have problem areas
   A 'mint', if you suffer from redness

2. *Cleansers (cream or lotion), tonic and moisturizer.*
   To suit your skin type
   Eye make-up remover (optional)

3. *Blushers, shapers and highlighters.*
At least one of each, either cream or
powder, depending on whether you
prefer to shape before or after applying your face powder. Ideally, you
should have two blushers, one on the
pink side, the other coral, to tone with
eyeshadows of different colours (pink
with blue, coral with brown, etc.)

4. *Translucent face powder.*
Loose; compressed into a compact; or
both

5. *Eyeshadows (compressed powder) and
shadow pencils.*
Several colours, with accompanying
highlighters, keyed to your wardrobe.
Additional pencils (more vivid in
colour, if you like) for lining inside
lower rims

6. *Eyebrow pencils.*
One colour (or perhaps, two for mixing) to tone with your hair

7. *Mascara.*
Block or wand; the latter, with or
without filaments
Possibly one with filaments for evening, one without for day

8. *Eyeliner* (optional).

9. *False lashes* (optional).

10. *Lip pencils.*

11. *Lipsticks.*
Several colours, keyed to your wardrobe. These should include one pink,
one red, one brown and one very pale;
with this selection, you can mix to
achieve almost any lip colour.

Tools

1. *Hand mirror.*

2. *Magnifying mirror.*

3. *Tweezers.*

4. *Hairclips, combs or covered elastic
band*
(to hold hair when making up).

5. *Sponges.*
Natural or foam-rubber, for applying
foundation (about two inches in
diameter)

6. *Eyelash curler* (optional).

7. *Pencil sharpener* (optional).

8. *Brushes.*
As many as you may need
Remember, long handles. The first
three should be round and bushy, not
flat
Powder brush (approximately two
inches wide)
Blusher/shader (approximately one
and one-half to two inches wide)
Highlighter (approximately one inch
wide)
Eyeshadow – two, one for shadows,
one for highlighters. (Flat, square-
ended. Approximately one-quarter
inch or three-eighths of an inch wide.
No wider)
Eyeliner (extremely fine and pointed)
Lip (pointed and filbert-shaped or
flat-ended)
Extra mascara brush, for separating
lashes (old wand will do)
Eyebrow (firm and stiff. Old clean
mascara brush will do)

9. *Applicators.*
Foam rubber, for eyeshadow (at least
two)

10. *Powder puffs.*
At least two, double-sided velour (so
you always have a dry one while the
other is being washed). Alternatively,
little squares of soft, old towelling

11. *Extras.*
Cleansing tissues
Cotton wool (in balls, or in rolls from
which you cut squares; it's wasteful to
tear them off)
Cotton swabs
Eyelash glue
Freshen-up pads

Perfumes and colognes

I shall discuss these in Chapter 12, because they are accessories, not make-up. You will, however, want to array your entire collection on your dressing-table or on a bathroom shelf, wherever you do your finishing touches. Be sure this place is neither hot nor in direct sunlight. Keep unopened bottles in the fridge.

Cleanliness is next to . . .

Let me remind you again of what I said in Chapter 6 about how important it is to keep your sponges clean and antiseptic (washed, and rinsed in an odourless disinfectant). The rest of your gear must also be immaculate, but other things don't need washing nearly so often. Powder puffs can get away with only once every week or ten days.

As for your brushes, the blusher/shader need never be washed at all. The ones you use for shadows, liners and lipstick, however, should be cleaned once a month or so. First, ease any excess shadow or lipstick out of the hairs with your fingers. Then, with a mild detergent or a bar of soap, work the suds thoroughly through the hairs. Do not pull against the direction in which they are attached to the handle, and don't twist or tangle them. Rinse well, and squeeze them dry with a paper towel, making certain that the hairs lie smooth. Finally, dip the brushes into a few drops of face-moisturizer to put back the natural oils that washing tends to remove. Ooze the moisturizer out again with your fingertips. As soon as the brushes are dry, they're ready to use.

At work

Women whose offices or other places of business are almost second homes, and who frequently go straight from work to dressy evening engagements, should keep (in a desk-drawer or a locker) a mini-collection of the basics they keep at home, from cleansers to mascara and cologne. The range can be much smaller – probably only two or three of the eyeshadow and lipstick shades you wear most often, and only the most important brushes.

Quite aside from cosmetics, you should also have emery boards, orange sticks and nail varnish (see Chapter 10); face freshening pads; a toothbrush and toothpaste; a spray mouth-freshener; indigestion tablets; eyedrops; a sharp knife for sharpening pencils; needle and cottons in several colours and a few safety pins.

In your handbag

Day or evening, you always want to carry with you a skeleton kit. You are not likely to need a complete new face, but you will inevitably want to touch up a bit. What your kit comprises will vary in colour, but not in content, from day to day, depending on your outfit. Obviously, you will need to carry more for a full day away from home, than for a few hours out in the evening.

The basics should include a tiny container (an old powder-eyeshadow compact, for instance) filled with cream foundation, in case your nose gets so shiny that face powder on its own won't do. In addition: face powder (loose, or compressed in a compact with a mirror); eyeshadow colour of the day, with its own little wand; lipstick colour of the day; lip-brush; one lip and one brow pencil. You will probably want a blusher, but you would rarely need a highlighter or shaper. Mascara, too, if you like to keep lashing it on when you are out. Otherwise, skip it.

And don't forget the odd extras: mouth-spray; eyedrops; face freshening pads; indigestion tablets, and safety pins. The day you leave any one of those out is the day you will need it most!

9. Hair: you and your hairdresser, home-care, problems

Your hair is your most important piece of apparel. Apparel? Of course. How often do people say, 'I like the way you *wear* your hair'? As much as your clothing, it expresses your personal style. The 'all-together woman', that paragon I have been talking about, knows how to put the two together – hair and clothing – to achieve a look of total unity.

Hair can be your greatest single asset. But it can be your greatest foe if you neglect it.

Hair today, like make-up, is natural-looking. It is seldom plastered down or tightly set. It looks alive. It moves, as freely as grain when a light breeze sweeps across it.

You must decide what you *want* your hair to do for you, and what it is *capable* of doing. Sad to say, the two don't always coincide. It is no good yearning for pale, fine, wavy hair if yours is coarse, straight and dark. Of course, you can give it some curl if it has none, and transform it from brown to gold or red. But there is nothing on earth that you can do to alter the texture of each individual hair, or the thickness of the total. Make peace with yourself. Don't fight desperately to attain the unattainable.

Think carefully: 'What exactly do I have on the top of my head?' In your personal inventory (see Chapter 2), you have answered all the relevant questions.

You know your hair's nature, colour and character. You know whether you have tortured it to distraction with too much bleach and too many perms.

Before we get to problems, let us consider style. Does yours suit you? Does it help you look as good as you can? Or does it ruin your appearance?

It is pointless to be in the vanguard of fashion if the fashion is not for you. Now, don't misunderstand me. I am all in favour of keeping up with trends. I am even happier if I am ahead of them. But not all the wild horses of all the Wild West could force me to wear my hair in an unbecoming style simply because some arbiter of fashion declared that it was 'in'. Nor in a style that my hair did not take to easily.

Perhaps you can meet fashion half-way. A reasonable approximation of what 'everybody is wearing' can usually be worked out, to accord with your type of hair and with your personality.

If you are too tall, too short, too fat or too skinny, you will obviously choose a style that detracts from the fault, rather than emphasizes it. It must help your figure.

And it must help your face. Your face, as you know (see Chapter 5), probably combines a couple of basic shapes. Take the two extremes, very long and very round. The general rules for these will, with common-sense modifications, guide you for all the face-shapes in between.

long face – wrong style

round face – wrong style

long face – correct style

round face – correct style

Long face

You usually have a long neck too, so you must counteract the vertical. Avoid a centre parting. Avoid skewering your hair tightly on top of your head. Avoid wearing it long and straight, clinging to your lean cheeks. The best length for a very long face is usually at about the level of your jaw.

A soft, loose wave will add width. A fringe will help counteract the forehead's height.

Round face

Your neck is usually short, so you must counteract the horizontal.

Avoid wearing your hair flat on top of your head. Avoid fluffing it out at the sides.

A softly curling fringe – but *only* at the temples, not all the way across your brow – will narrow your forehead. Any trick you can play to add height at the crown will draw attention away from the roundness. Have your hair cut in layers, with the shortest layers on the top. If it is very pale in colour, darken it slightly, or add a reddish glint.

Bad features

If your ears are ugly, keep them covered. No matter what the shape of your face, you can subtly modify your style.

If you have a double chin, don't pull your hair back to disclose the entire jaw. Let it fall lightly round your cheeks.

If you have an extremely low hairline, a soft, short fringe will detract from the scowling Mrs Caveman look. I know that is a surprising suggestion. But you create an optical illusion by blurring the edges, which suggests that the fringe starts a good deal higher up.

If you have a long nose or a large nose, you need the help of softly flowing hair and gentle lines to detract from it. You should never pull your hair tightly back from your face. Nor should you go to the other extreme and wear it long and straight, like curtains. Both make the fault more obvious.

You and your hairdresser

Bad hairdressers are as much use as measles. Good ones should be weighed in carats. Some of their prices these days make you think that they actually are. Still, no money you spend is better spent than on a first-rate, properly styled hair-cut.

I don't mean that you must scurry off to the most expensive hairdresser in town. I do mean that you should skimp on something else, if necessary, to pay for the best you can afford. In the long run, this saves money.

Because of inflation, fewer and fewer women now have their hair set every week as they used to do. No one knows this better and feels the pinch harder than the salon-keeper. Consequently, he has grown accustomed to the idea that he must cut and style your hair skilfully enough so that you can care for it yourself between visits. And that your visits may be as far apart as five or six weeks –

only when you need another trim or cut.

That, of course, puts a great chunk of the burden on you. You must learn as much as you can about hair-do-it-yourself. I shall pass along some tricks of the trade, but the most practical way for you to pick them up is by watching your hairdresser. Watch where and how he places the rollers; where he uses clips; how he holds the blow-dryer and moves the brush. Keep asking him 'Why?' He'll be glad to tell you; it is for his benefit as well as yours.

You and he should work as a team. The first time you walk into his salon, you know a great deal more about your hair than he does. Certainly, he will be able to tell by look and by touch if it is out of condition, if it has been badly permed or badly dyed. But you can't expect him to be a mind-reader. How will he know that your set always drops out after only twenty-four hours? Or that your hair goes hysterical when the weather's humid? Or that you wash it every day in a futile non-stop battle against oiliness? Help him to help you.

When you book your appointment, ask for an operator who is particularly good with your kind of hair or problem. Go armed: know what you are talking about, and you'll be able to determine whether what he suggests is sensible, or just a load of rubbish.

Your hairdresser should explain not only what he intends to do, but how you should keep up the good work in between, with conditioner, shampoo or whatever.

Hairdressers are like the rest of the human race. Most are honest. But there is never any harm in treading carefully. You will probably have chosen your salon because a friend has recommended it, or because it has a good reputation. Chances are that you're in safe hands. However, it is your money, so don't part with it unless you are certain that you're getting what you want and need.

Don't sit there like a nincompoop and

say yes to everything. Don't let anyone lop your hair off short unless you genuinely want it short. Don't be talked into a change of colour unless you have thought about it and planned it in advance. Don't do anything on impulse. It can take months for the damage to be undone.

Do, however, take good advice. Listen to the clever stylist who tells you why he thinks a fringe would suit you, who explains that the only way to get rid of the split ends is to trim them off. Heed the words of the practised colourist who says that you would look better with warm, rich brown than with bright red.

Above all, harken to the wise expert who cautions against having a perm and either a bleach or a dye at the same time. If you want your hair to fall out, this combination is almost guaranteed to do it.

If you are trying a new place for the first time, book for a shampoo and set only. You may get a turn-down from a top salon. Many refuse to set any head they haven't styled themselves. I can't say I blame them. They don't want to risk their hard-won reputations by letting Mrs Jones swagger about with an atrocious cut and bragging, 'I had my hair done at Mr X's.'

The little chap (or girl) around the corner is almost always willing to do no more than a shampoo and set. He might turn out to have been exceedingly well trained, and be just as good for you, at half the price, as the Big Name on the high street.

A visit to the hairdresser should give you pleasure. There are a number of things besides good work which you have the right to expect:

1. *Promptness.* To be kept waiting for five or ten minutes, especially if the delay is combined with an apology and an explanation, is forgivable. Once in a while, that is, not always. But it is mad-dening to be left sitting for half an hour or more before you start; or with your head wrapped in a towel after you've been shampooed; or roasting under the dryer beyond the normal time it takes your hair to dry. (You know how long that should be. If you have been plopped down and ignored, tap the elbow of whoever is passing, and ask to be taken out.)

2. *Cleanliness.* Don't accept a dirty gown. You can refuse politely, suggest perhaps that it was given to you by mistake. If that is how the salon starts, God save you from their hairdressing. Ditto for towels. These probably won't actually look dirty, but if the one that's put round your shoulders feels suspiciously damp, there's a reasonable chance that it has been on someone else's shoulders first.

3. *Fresh combs and brushes.* Is there a sterilizer? Is it actually being used? Or is it merely on display to kid you into believing that the place is hygienic?

4. *Service.* A junior should bring you a choice of magazines (preferably not a million years old) while you are waiting for your operator or sitting under the dryer. If you want a cup of coffee, it should come quickly – and hot – and not in a chipped cup. (Small salons which haven't the facilities to provide this service will send out to the nearest café.)

Here is a money-saving tip, a particularly good stunt if you are young and broke. Many of the best, high-priced salons run training courses for their staff, often in the evenings, for which they need guinea pigs. As a volunteer piglet, you are charged little more than the cost of the materials, possibly as little as a quarter of the salon's regular price.

You are not required to settle for anything you don't want, and nothing drastic is likely to go amiss. The teacher, like a surgeon with his trainee medicos, is there to guarantee that no one makes an incision in the wrong place. On the other hand, wonderful things might happen. You can come away cut, styled, tinted or permed. If the 'master' is evolving something entirely new, you could emerge way, way ahead of fashion.

When I was in my teens I had my hair done frequently at training schools. I didn't always crow with glee over the results, but I was never unhappy. And I learned an awful lot about my own hair, and about how to handle other people's.

Doing your own hair

Shampoo

Your hair, no matter what its type, must be washed at least once a week. It's not the end of the world if you sometimes let it slip to eight or nine days. Longer than that, what with perspiration, grease, pollution, make-up and so on, and it gets really disgusting. Blonde and grey hair, like light-coloured clothes, actually show the dirt, and usually have to be washed more often. Greasy hair may need it every day.

There are 'ifs' and 'buts' to all of this. Suppose your hair is both light-coloured and dry. Frequent washing will intensify the dryness. Brush it daily, which gets rid of surface dirt and also stimulates the oils, and keep the shampoos down to once a week. Or go on with your twice-weekly ritual, but instead of using two doses of shampoo (as almost all makes direct you to do), skip the second.

With oily hair, it is possible to wean yourself away from the daily scrubbing. And 'scrubbing' is the operative word. What I said about oily skin (see Chapter 4) and how the terrible tendency to treat it brutally only makes it worse, also holds true for hair. If you use a harsh anti-grease shampoo too often, and pummel your scalp as though it were your enemy, the sebaceous glands will over-react. The result: more oiliness, not less. So, once again, gently does it.

You may benefit by switching to a shampoo designed for 'normal'. Whatever you buy, be certain that it is non-detergent, and wash with coolish water, not scalding hot. One more thing: be sure that your *entire* head needs washing before you douse it all. The oil could be only on your fringe, or at the ends. Section off with a comb the bit that is greasy and, with a little shampoo fluffed on your fingertips, wash that section only.

Detergent shampoos are a danger for everyone. They are drying and harmful. Unfortunately, there are all too many on the market. Even more unfortunately, there is seldom a consultant on hand where hair products are sold to advise you on what you should or should not buy. You are faced with a baffling array of shampoos – herbal, lemon, egg, cream, almond, medicated – you name it.

What is a poor girl to do? *First*, buy the correct shampoo for your hair-type (bearing in mind the reservations above for 'oily'). The bottle should say for 'dry' or 'normal' or 'oily'. *Second*, when you are trying any new shampoo, buy a sachet, not an enormous bottle. If you hate it, you have spent very little. If you love it, go back for the large economy size. *Third*, if you suspect that your shampoo contains detergent, do the litmus-paper test that you did with your bubble bath (see Chapter 4).

There is a growing school of thought which recommends baby shampoos for everyone, unless you have some particular condition which calls for a specialized shampoo. How can you go wrong with what is mild enough for a baby?

Don't ever rub a bar of soap directly on to your hair. If you have run out of shampoo, and only soap is handy, then grate a bit into a cup of warm water and let it sit until it is liquefied.

Washing

The best place to wash your hair is under the shower. If you don't have one, use a spray attached to the taps of your wash-basin. It is impossible to get all the shampoo out by rinsing in the basin. It is even worse to dip your head back into your own bath-water. Ugh! All that does is mix what has come off your body with what has come off your hair. If you can't be dissuaded from washing your hair in the bath (I wish you could be), then you really must use a spray – not only to rinse your hair, but to sluice your body.

Just before you shampoo, stand with your head bent down and give your hair a brisk brushing. The hundred strokes that grandma swore by is not one stroke too many. This brings the blood to your scalp, and it spreads the natural oils all the way down to the ends. Needless to say, you do *not* do it if your hair is greasy.

I like to measure out from my big shampoo bottle, into a small plastic container (say, a clean yoghurt carton) the exact amount I need for my two washes. I mix it with a little warm water to start it diluting. I do the same with my conditioner – when I use one – and set that little pot on the opposite side of the basin. Groping around with my eyes closed, and with water streaming down my face, I can put my hands on what I want. No danger of picking up the wrong thing, or of using too much or too little.

Wet your hair completely with water of a comfortable temperature. For the first wash, use only a little shampoo. Massage it through thoroughly, working your fingers underneath, both back and front, as well as on top. This is particularly important with long hair.

Many first-rate shampoos these days do not whip up into foam. Don't let that worry you. That whipped-cream look matters only psychologically. It is not the foam that does the job; it is the pro-duct itself. You can tell by the feel when the shampoo is well worked through.

Flush away every last trace of shampoo with clean water. Then give it a second load. As before: complete massage, complete rinse. After you think all the soapiness is gone, rinse it once again. A third washing is almost never necessary – not unless your hair has been dirty for far too long. Finish off, if you can bear it, with a blast of cold water. Terrific for the scalp.

Conditioners

Follow your shampoo with a conditioner, if you need one. Not all of us do. Some need them only on the ends.

Most conditioners are similar in effect to the liquid you put into the last rinse of the family wash. Softening. Smoothing. Certain varieties are actually treatments, formulated to counteract dryness, for instance, or to control dandruff. The ordinary conditioner merely coats the hair and gives it a pleasing texture; it does not work its way inside to offer any long-lasting help. It will make your hair easier to comb. It will keep it from going wild. It will improve the look of split ends.

The more your hair has been damaged, the more good a conditioner will do. If you have permed or bleached repeatedly, you would be horrified were you to look at a single strand under a microscope. Its surface will be frayed and frazzled like an old piece of rope. The conditioner smooths all those raggedy bits down flat, sort of sticks them together.

If your hair has never been mistreated, it probably doesn't need a conditioner. In fact, it won't willingly accept one. It will slide off like water off that proverbial duck's back. It may indeed make hair which is ordinarily manageable suddenly fly away, out of control.

Buy a conditioner, as you do a shampoo, with a trial sachet first. Follow the instructions. Most will tell you to massage it in, and then to leave it for about two minutes before rinsing. A few require no rinsing. So read before you begin.

Some women like to rinse with diluted lemon juice; others swear by rainwater. The first adds a glint to blonde hair, but it is acid and can therefore have a drying effect. As for rainwater, if you live in a big city or near a rail-line or a motorway, or under a jet flight-path, no – a thousand times no! It can put more dirt back into your hair than you have just washed out.

Don't underestimate the power – the danger – of any old-fashioned home rinse or other treatment. Just because you keep something in the kitchen doesn't mean it is safe for your hair. Egg yolks: okay. Almond, coconut or olive oil: of course. Vinegar: maybe. Herbs: rosemary and camomile are fine, but don't slap any old herb on to your head because you like the way it tastes in your stew.

In general, it is wiser to stick with manufactured products which have been laboratory-tested.

Drying and setting

Quickly towel-dry your hair to get rid of the dripping. But leave some moisture; that makes it easier to handle. Whether you blow-dry or set it in rollers or both, comb it through, putting in your parting and generally coaxing it into the shape it will finally have.

There are two exceptions: if your hair has been permed to give you squiggly little curls all over, simply run your fingers through it and leave it to dry on its own. If your hair has a beautiful natural wave, you may be able to comb it into place and let it dry unaided.

Setting lotions   Arguments for and against these have raged for decades.

The tendency in good salons these days is *not* to use them. A well-cut head of hair in reasonably good condition usually doesn't need one, and looks softer and more natural without it. Extremely fine, straight or unruly hair may profit from a very little very light lotion – strong enough only to keep it in place, not a thick gluey gunk that prevents it from moving. With extraordinarily thin hair, you can use a so-called 'thickening' lotion which coats the strands slightly and adds body. ('Beer?' you ask. You have always used it? If you like it, go on doing so. It can't do any harm.)

Blow-dry   Unless your hair is naturally curly, in which case you can get away with blowing it rather casually, and simply sweeping it into place as you go, you must control and direct your dryer with precision. Never, never hold it nearer to your head than four or five inches. Too much heat, too close, injures both hair and scalp.

Divide your hair into sections, and dry each separately. Pin back the bits that you are not working on, so that they don't get blown about. Begin at the *bottom* of the *back*, and, holding your brush with one hand and your dryer with the other, swirl the undermost layer into position. Keep brushing until it is exactly where you want it and until you are certain that it is dry.

Work up, one layer at a time, to a line across the back of your head that runs approximately from ear to ear. Then go on to the sides, and finally to the front, again working from the undermost layer.

To give your hair a wavy lilt, lift it high upwards from the scalp with your brush. If you want it to lie straight, or if you are trying to overcome natural waviness, then you must grip the hair with the brush from underneath, and stretch it tightly as you dry it. There is a knack to all this which you can master with practice. If you are having trouble, ask your hairdresser to let you have a go under his supervision. Nothing more may be wrong than the way you hold your brush.

Rollers The size of roller you use depends upon the degree of curl you want and the amount of hair you put in each. Big rollers, each holding a large skein of hair, result in big, loose waves; small rollers, each holding a little hair, result in tighter, smaller curls. You may, according to your style, need a combination of the two, possibly with some rolling forward, others backward. For ends too short to roll, use flat clips. Watch what your hairdresser does. Ask him why. Then do likewise.

With rollers, you section off in the same way as when you blow-dry. But you work in the reverse direction, starting from the *top* of the *front* and gradually moving down and around to the bottom of the back.

Never try to wind a larger hank of hair on to a roller than it can easily hold. Comb the section you are about to curl with a tail-comb. Then, holding the hair *straight up* from the roots, wind it with your fingers smoothly and tightly around the roller. I want to emphasize that. Straight up. Vertically from the roots. This provides the lift you need for natural, bouncy movement. Be careful not to let any stray bits dangle out. Feed these into place with the tail of your comb.

Your set will be only as good as the way you put your rollers in. That is what makes the biggest difference between an amateur and a professional hair-do.

Pin the first roller into place with a hairpin. Pin the second tightly to the first, and so on. It isn't necessary to be able to see the back while you are working on it. You can tell by feel whether or not the hair is smooth, and if you have left any loose straggles. But double-check when you have finished by a glance into your hand mirror.

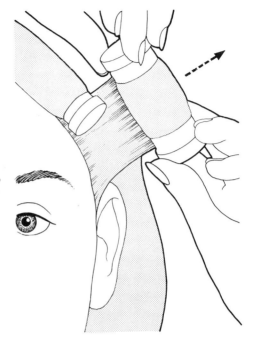

Tie a loose net around your head before you dry it. The chief reason is that it keeps your rollers from flopping out of position, or from falling out altogether. It also helps prevent the breeze from ruffling your hair unduly. Then dry as you please – with a blow-dryer or under a hood.

Don't take your rollers out before your hair is absolutely dry. Test one, where your hair is longest and thickest. Let it cool (the heat will delude you into thinking it's dry when it isn't), unroll it carefully and feel along the entire length. If the slightest dampness remains, re-roll, be patient and dry for a little longer. After the trouble you have just taken, don't ruin it all by rushing.

Once the rollers are out, brush your hair *against* the direction in which you have put them in. Brush from underneath as well as on the surface. This loosens the hair and gets rid of any demarcation lines left from your sectioning or from the rollers themselves. Then brush it in the right direction, and, using comb or brush as needed, dress it in its final style.

If your hair is very thin, or if it could do with a little extra width or extra height, you can finish off with a discreet amount of back-combing beneath the top layer. Pick up a few strands of hair and, holding them with your fingertips, ruffle them slightly by pulling your comb back and forth a couple of times. Don't be aggressive about it. A mere touch adds body. More than that, and you end up with a mass of tangles. Absolute agony to comb out, and not very good for your hair. When you have finished, smooth the surface over the base which the back-combing has provided.

Heated rollers　With easily manageable hair, and for certain styles – only the hint of a wave, perhaps – you can speed up the entire process by blow-drying and then styling with heated electric rollers. The same rules apply for these as for regular rollers: front first; hair held vertically from the scalp; all ends neatly tucked in.

You will remember, by the way, that I suggested in Chapter 1, under Celia's Second Law, that you can accomplish two things at once by wearing heated rollers while you bathe. Indeed you can. With two provisos.

If your hair is very curly (by perm or by nature), the combination of steam and hot rollers might make it frizzy. You are better off to put the rollers in cold, and count on the steam alone to provide the needed warmth.

If your hair is straight, and steam makes it go lank, wearing rollers in your bath won't give you a proper wave. All that you can expect them to do is to help prevent a fringe or longish ends from dropping.

You must not, under any circumstances, fall into the habit of using heated rollers too often. They can be over-drying, and they may split the ends. Exceptionally strong hair can tolerate them three to four times a week. Fine hair, especially if it is on the dry side, cannot put up with them more often than twice a week. If you find yourself relying upon them constantly, you would probably be better off with a soft permanent wave.

Not for you? You must go on with your rollers? Then here's a trick (a bit fidgety to do, but worth doing) to avoid split ends. Clip off all the sharp prongs from the rollers; they are what cause the split ends. Then take thin foam-rubber, and sew a little jacket for each. This, instead of the prongs, will keep them in place. Alternatively, wrap them in tissue paper. (Not quite so good at gripping, of course, and you will have to re-wrap frequently.)

Hairspray　With a good hair-cut – properly shaped and properly layered – you should not need one. However, there are exceptions (aren't there always?). If your hair is truly unmanageable and nothing but spray keeps it in place, then be sure to buy the kind that *brushes out*, and don't use it any more often than absolutely necessary. It can be drying.

Spray attracts grime the way incomes attract tax. So you must wash your hair more often. Is the spray really helpful enough to make it worth the trouble?

To control fine, dry, fly-away hair, I am much happier about creamy conditioners. There are several good varieties which are extremely light in texture. Use only a tiny blob. Rub it between your palms, smooth it on and comb it through.

To tint or not to tint

Why not indeed? So long as you know what you're doing. Nature is not entirely stupid, and your own hair colour is likely to be appropriate to your complexion. Nature, however, can sometimes be unreasonably dictatorial, and what she has accorded you does not necessarily rule out another, equally appropriate, colour. Nor does it rule out merely giving your own extra warmth and verve, instead of making any drastic change.

Certain kinds of hair react gratifyingly. There is no reason to go through life with hair that is mousey, that is neither blonde nor brown, neither one thing nor another. Nor with hair that is going grey and not doing it very smartly.

That indeterminate salt-and-pepper colour or the dowdy yellowing which sometimes occurs when brown or blonde hair starts to grey can be most misery-making. Of course, something should be done about it. But not anything ridiculous! One of the saddest sights in the world to me is the woman who thinks that she disguises her age by dying her hair an outlandish colour.

Change yours, by all means, but don't try to go back to the shade you were when you were a girl. Your skin has changed since then. Your hairdresser might suggest a few reddish highlights, or striking black streaks, perhaps. You might try a medium-brown rinse. Or have your hair ever so slightly bleached to a soft, silvery blonde.

Please, though, I beg of you, don't be tempted by mauve, pink or blue rinses. They really do shriek 'ageing lady!' just as surely as does middle-age spread or wearing the same bright blue eyeshadow you have worn for the last fifteen years.

If, however, you are going grey dramatically, say, white temples or natural streaks of white on dark hair, I wouldn't change it for the world. I wouldn't, and I didn't. My hair used to be black, and it started to turn white when I was in my early teens. At first I wore a long black hair-piece, and then (what a confession; I must have been mad) I touched up my silvering fringe with mascara!

Common sense finally took over. Not only did I learn to live with it. I learned to love it. (My husband says he'll leave me if I change it.) I am still in my early thirties, and the white hair is a plus for me. I may reconsider in a dozen years or so, but I doubt it. Some of the ageing women I most admire, I admire because of their heads of handsome well-groomed grey hair. A few undoubtedly get occasional help from a rinse to counteract any tendency to yellowness. The result is splendid.

No matter what your hair colour, don't do anything over-bold at the start. If you are hankering for a change, why not begin with a few highlighting streaks? Several slightly red strands or a few gleaming blonde ones can make an amazing difference to dull drab hair. Or have a trial run with a rinse before you go in for a dye. A brunette might be absolutely stunning if her hair were red. Then again, she might look awful.

It isn't easy to be certain in advance. But your hairdresser and his colourist should advise. They should say a stern no if you ask for something outrageous.

You can, of course, give yourself a 'preview' by trying on a few wigs in the shades you are considering. (I am not suggesting that you buy one. There are other, better things to do with your money. But this will let you see whether what you have in mind will bring delight or disaster.)

Save heartbreak by having any colour-change, no matter how slight, done in two easy stages. Yes, though it be only from mole-brown to rich brown. It is no more costly. You will need the second colouring eventually anyway, and by then you will have lived with the new tone long enough to feel confident about taking it one step further. You might even decide to leap on to the third step, by perhaps adding a little auburn.

Which brings me to another consideration. You undertake a commitment whenever you change your hair-colour. It is both time-consuming and expensive. After a few weeks – three to four, on average – your natural colour begins to show at the roots, and you cannot postpone the retouching. With bleaching or dyeing, you could also be letting yourself in for problems like dryness and brittleness, which will require constant attention.

Can you tint it yourself?

Yes, up to a point. You can quite easily give yourself a rinse that washes out. The worst thing that can happen is that you don't like it and – well – you wash it out.

without perm

with perm

If you are *extremely* careful, you can also use a permanent colourant at home. Be certain that you buy a product made by a reputable manufacturer. Be certain of your colour choice. Be certain that you follow instructions to the letter.

Dyeing your own hair is a messy process. It demands patience and fortitude. If I were doing it, especially for the first time, I would get a friend to help me. How about a trade of skills? Your chum gives you a hand, and you bake her a cake.

Streaks and highlights are best done by the professional. Even more so is this true of bleaching the entire head. Bleaches can be stronger than you think and work much faster. A mistake may lead to wretchedness. If your budget won't permit a bleach in a dependable salon, I honestly think that compromise is indicated. Wouldn't a slight change of tone which you can safely achieve yourself be a far, far better thing than taking a dangerous risk?

Perms

The permanent wave has become a wonderous thing. Used with skill, it is astonishingly flexible. You can have a soft wave or a tight curl. You can have part of your head done one way, part another. You can confine the perm to stubborn ends or to a recalcitrant fringe. As your hair grows, the curl will gradually flatten near the roots, but even so, a well-done wave should last about six months.

If you can afford it, you should have it done professionally. The results are infinitely better and more predictable. And, most important of all, less risky! A perm demands both expertise and knowledge. The professional knows what difficulties he may encounter, and how to deal with them. You cannot be so sure. I have seen home-perms applied to thin or bleached hair which ended in calamity – the worst of these, a headful of short, bristly, broken ends.

113

If you are determined to have a go, you are better off than you would have been a few years ago. There are a number of products now available for home-use which are not hit-or-miss the way the old ones used to be. The best are time-controlled, so that even if you are forgetful, or fall asleep, the action will stop before it can harm your hair. Some are packed in aerosols which you spray on.

Investigate before you buy. Then buy the safest product you can, and follow the instructions in every detail. But – a big BUT, this one – don't imagine that giving yourself a perm is a cinch. It is more troublesome and considerably more demanding than a home-dye. So (yes, again) call on a friend for help.

Problems

Your hair is a kind of barometer. Look at it. Feel it. Watch for warning signals. It could be that your hair alone is heading for trouble. It could be more serious – that something is wrong with your health. Just like a cat's coat. When puss isn't well, her fur goes dull and rough.

Hair is not alive. The only life is in the roots. Lustrous and glowing though it may look when it is at its best, it is completely dead. Consequently, when anything goes wrong, it must be treated from the roots up. Or, if it is a medical problem, from within.

If your hairdresser cannot diagnose the trouble, he may advise a visit to a trichologist. A consultation with such a hair-problem specialist can be costly, but if your man knows what he is doing, he is worth it. He might, in turn, suggest that you see your doctor. It could be a matter of diet, of circulation or of nervous strain.

Split ends and exceedingly dry hair

The two usually go together. The chief villains are over-bleaching, over-

perming, detergent shampoos and too much exposure to the sun. This last is particularly harmful if you have wetted your hair repeatedly with sea water. Combs or brushes that are too harsh can also cause split ends. The only way to get rid of them is to have them trimmed off.

An oil treatment may help combat over-dryness. It doesn't work for everyone, but it's worth a try. A couple of hours before you shampoo, comb a natural oil (almond, olive and coconut are all excellent) through your hair. Rub it well into your scalp, tuck your hair into a plastic bag and wrap it with a dry towel. (The plastic is to protect the towel from becoming an oily mess.) The longer you leave it on, the better.

Sitting under a dryer for a while makes the treatment even more effective. So does wrapping your head in a steaming-hot wet towel – re-heating the towel when it cools, and wrapping again two or three times. Again, don't forget the plastic bag.

When you wash the oil off, put the shampoo directly onto your hair and work it through with your fingers before you wet it. If you put the water on first, the oil will resist it.

Oiliness

This is almost invariably no one's fault but nature's. You can make it worse, as I have said, by being too tough. A final cold rinse after your shampoo with a little lemon juice (nothing harsher) can be beneficial.

Dry scalp

Not to be confused with dandruff (see below). Occasional falling flecks of white can be a sign of nothing more serious than that you haven't rinsed your shampoo out thoroughly. If the flecking is more persistent, the cause could be a detergent shampoo. It might be the sign of an allergy to some hair product; if you are using anything you haven't tried before, merely giving it up may clear the condition. Dry scalp can also result from blow-drying too close to your head or from using heated rollers too often. An oil treatment (as above) may help.

It sometimes occurs with nervous tension – much harder to pin down, much harder to cure. Relaxing, taking life easy is the answer, which is far more easily said than done.

Dandruff

An infection, not merely an annoying inconvenience. It is itchy, unpleasant and can cause sore, red patches. It occurs far more frequently with oily scalps and greasy hair than with dry. It is stubborn and contagious.

Medicated shampoos sometimes do a little good, but, unfortunately, usually only for the first use or two. Then your scalp becomes accustomed to them and begins to resist them. Your chemist sells dandruff-treatment preparations (seldom prettily packaged, they are very down-to-earth) which can be a great deal more effective than medicated shampoos.

A trichologist should be able to help. If your circumstance is truly dreadful, he may advise you to talk it over with your doctor, who will probably send you on to a dermatologist, a skin specialist.

Falling hair

You lose a few hairs every day, which are replaced by new ones. Perfectly normal. Should you suddenly see more on your comb than your daily ration, should it begin to come out in handfuls, then you may have something serious to worry about. Possibly, you have bleached or permed too often.

This could be the symptom of a health problem. You may be reacting badly to a course of medication. It may be the result of a foolish crash-diet. Don't dither about it. Find out at once. If your

hairdresser doesn't have the answer, your doctor should.

Combs and brushes

The most important thing I have to say about combs is one single DON'T. Don't ever use a metal one. It can harm the surface of the hair and it can break the ends.

Of course, tortoise-shell or ivory (who can afford them?) are nicer than plastic. But there's nothing wrong with plastic combs, as long as they are well-made, with no jaggedy, raggedy edges. Broad-toothed combs are better for your hair than fine ones. You should own at least one tail-comb, plus your ordinary straight combs for dressing-table and handbag.

As for brushes, it is no longer true that all that is not bristle is bad. Many synthetic ones are now excellent, and some of the best – the swirly ones which most hairdressers use – are made of a combination of bristle and synthetic fibres. Do, however, avoid cheap nylon brushes with rough-cut straight ends. They can rip your hair brutally.

Never tug your brush through your hair. Ease it through a knot or a tangle. Roughness will only cause trouble.

Wash your combs and brushes (in the same shampoo you use on your head, or in a mild detergent) every time you wash your hair. And as Polonius said in another connection, 'Neither a borrower nor a lender be.'

'My hair looks ghastly'

It can happen to the best of us, usually when it is due for a shampoo. There is no point in merely letting it hang limply around your shoulders, while you moan, 'I really must wash it tomorrow.'

If it is long, put it up in a bun or tie it into a pony-tail. You can wear a false plait or a fall, with the lank ends artfully pinned underneath.

If it is short, tuck the uncontrollable bits up neatly with an attractive comb or two.

If it is clinging flatly to your head, add a bit of body with a tiny amount of back-combing. (Sorry. This won't work if it's greasy.)

If it isn't good enough to be seen under any circumstances, cover it. In general, I am not happy about wigs. But, should you happen to own one, and should you be unable to think of a more ingenious alternative, then you may as well wear it. Only in absolute desperation, however – not every time you're feeling lazy.

I think it is a great deal brighter to swirl a scarf around your head. It becomes a positive fashion accessory, not a pathetic apology. One of the most elegant women I ever knew was a beauty editor, and she would come into her office every Friday morning wearing a scarf wound turban-style around her head, and always fastened with a handsome piece of jewellery. Under it, she was giving herself an all-day oil treatment, before she went to the hairdresser late in the afternoon. Between hair and scarf were a couple of layers of tissue paper.

Evening styles

Cast off your sensible daytime habits, and do the reverse of what you normally do. Use your imagination. You wear your hair tidily pinned up in a bun all day? Let it fall free and loose in the evening. You ordinarily let it hang to your shoulders? Then twirl it high on top of your head, or roll it into a chignon. Surprise yourself and everyone else by appearing with it curly in the evening when it is usually straight. Add a false plait. Or plait your own.

And dress it up. Wear sparkly slides or clips or a pair of pretty combs. Tie a head-band or ribbon round it, to match your dress. Or perch a circlet of tortoise-shell (plastic tortoise, that is) on your crown and bring your hair up at the sides around it. Assemble all your bits and pieces in advance – ribbons that exactly match what you're wearing, diamanté combs that go with your ear-rings.

Choose a style that suits your clothing and the occasion. It looks plain stupid to turn up at the disco in your jeans with a hair-do designed for a duchess at a sedate ball. Not only inappropriate, but utterly impractical. It will probably all come tumbling down as soon as you start to jiggle.

It's a smart move to practise any new style at least once before you present it to your public, especially if it involves a lot of pinning. Try it out at home. Move about. Dance. Run up and down stairs. If it straggles and starts to go astray, it is not quite as good an idea as you thought. Better to have the back descend when you are on your own, than to feel it come sliding down at the moment you are making your grand entrance.

(PS. When in doubt, for evening or any other time, you can never go wrong with clean, shining hair that swings freely.)

10. Hands and feet: care and comfort

Hands and feet – what important roles they play, not only because of all the things they do for us, but in our thinking. We are always giving someone a hand, putting a job in hand, grasping a bird in the hand. As for feet, do we not put our foot down, put our best foot forward, foot bills, get our foot in the door?

You owe it to them to keep them looking and feeling happy. Both (all four) should be tackled – manicured and pedicured – at least once a fortnight. Every week is better. Neglect them for as long as a month, and you're stuck with a tiresome, time-consuming task.

If you can manage a solid hour or so, do your hands and feet at the same time. You have all the gear laid out anyway, so why not take advantage? For women who must be misers with their minutes, however, it is sensible to alternate: hands one week, feet the next.

Hands

Only a lucky few are born with slim, pale smooth hands and perfectly shaped nails. What a tragedy when they, of all people, treat them shabbily! The rest of us are likely to have almost anything – short, squat, podgy fingers; lumpy fingers; bony, knobbly fingers; broad nails; brittle nails. But they can all look better than they are. Beautifully manicured hands suggest both youth and fastidiousness.

There is really no good reason for not having well-kept hands. House-work? That's no excuse for chipped polish, broken nails and rough red skin. Not when every supermarket and chemist shop will sell you rubber gloves to safeguard your hands and inexpensive nourishing creams or lotions to soothe them.

Wear protective gloves for all rough jobs, from turning out a grubby closet to washing dishes. Use a nail-brush, by all means, for your regular hand-washings, but not one with tough, stiff bristles. Keep jars or tubes of handcream beside the kitchen sink, by the washing machine, in the bathroom – wherever your hands come into contact with detergents, or even with soap and water. When you go out in the cold, wear gloves to stave off chilblains and chapping. Well-made gloves have chic; even mittens have a certain puppy-dog charm.

Do all that, and prettifying your hands becomes a relatively simple matter.

We are not all striving for the same ideal. Extremely long nails aren't right for everyone. They can add grace and elegance to a short, squat hand. On a large square hand, they seem enormous. On a long, skinny hand, they look like witch's talons. In some professions, they are utterly impractical – nursing or dentistry, for instance. Women with extremely brittle nails simply cannot grow them.

If you yearn for long nails, and for one reason or another, cannot make your own, false nails are a perfectly adequate substitute. Before I turn to false ones, let's see how best to look after those you have.

Manicure

Giving yourself a manicure is a fairly easy skill to master. And a very important skill, since salon manicures, like almost everything else we yearn for, have become rather costly. If you are a beginner, I'll suggest what I have with other kinds of beauty care: poach on the professional's territory. Treat yourself to a salon job – once. Watch carefully what the manicurist does, and don't hesitate to ask why.

Even if you never go near a salon, however, you'll soon pick up the knack.

Don't ever try to rush a manicure. Unless you have had a lot of practice, you'll need about half an hour. Twenty minutes, if you're a whiz. I always try to combine doing my nails with something else – that Law again. Something virtuous, like an oil treatment for my hair. (My head's already wrapped in a towel, and I want to give it plenty of time.) Or something utterly relaxing, like watching an old film on TV.

First assemble everything you are going to need:

A small hand towel
A bowl of warm water
Emery boards and orange sticks
Cotton wool
Oily nail varnish remover
Cuticle cream
Base coat
Nail varnish (and possibly varnish thinner)
Top coat (optional)
Quick-dry spray (optional)
OR
Instead of base coat and varnish, nail buffer, nail rouge and nail-whitening pencil

If you're going to varnish, you'll need a flat surface. I like to put a big, broad book on my lap and wrap it in my towel. You may find it easier to work on a table.

Removing Polish   Let us assume that you are starting with old varnish on your nails. That word 'varnish', by the way – don't let it confuse you. It's sometimes called 'polish', sometimes 'enamel'. All the same thing. By whatever name, your first step is to remove it completely.

On my list, I said *oily* remover. Be sure the label says 'oily'. There are a lot of inferior inexpensive products for sale which are basically nothing but raw acetone. They will remove the polish; they will do that very well. But they will also strip the surface of the nail; dry your cuticles mercilessly, and take the moisture out of your skin wherever they happen to touch. The difference in price between a kind remover and a cruel one is minimal, so don't save pennies this way.

Moisten a pad of cotton wool with the remover and press it down on all ten nails, one after another, holding it firmly for two or three seconds on each. That starts the polish dissolving. Then wipe over each nail again. By now the polish will have softened and it should come off easily. Take a fresh pad of cotton, moisten it with remover and go scrupulously over all ten nails until every last speck of polish is gone.

Rinse your hands quickly in your bowl of warm water to remove the remover. Dry them well.

'Why no soap in the water?' you ask. For a good reason. Soap is drying. Unless your hands are extremely dirty, you don't need it.

Filing   Even if you don't want to shorten your nails, you must file them. They are constantly being worn thin at the ends, and they will break or crack if you don't. Please use an emery board.

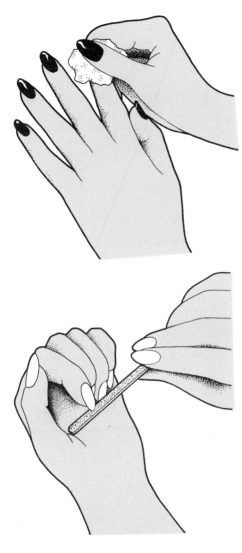

this too can rip your nails. And don't go too far down the sides: no further down than where the curve of the tip ends. Your nails need support to keep them from breaking, especially if you wear them long.

Naturally, you want them all to be of an even length. But if one is broken, it is a pity to file the other nine down to match it. Far better to apply a false nail (see p. 123) to the short one.

Once you have achieved the right shape and length, smooth the tips with the fine-grained side of the emery board. Again you work from sides to centre.

Cuticles Before I say what you should do, I shall say emphatically what you should not do. *Never, never trim cuticles with scissors or a clipper! Never cut round that troublesome crescent of skin!* To cut them will only make them grow back stronger and tougher. There is one exception. You can – in fact, you should – snip off a hang-nail. Otherwise you are tempted to tear at it or gnaw at it, which may give you a very sore finger indeed.

I don't go much for liquid cuticle removers, either. They are not quite as bad as scissors, but it stands to reason that if they're strong enough to take off that little layer of dead skin, they're too strong to be good for the live skin nearby. Give your cuticles a decent chance – hand cream whenever you wash, and lots before you go to bed – and they should never require brutal treatment.

So, back to your manicure. Dab a blob of cuticle cream (or a rich, nourishing face cream) on to the base of each nail, and massage it in. Put both hands into the bowl of warm water, and slosh your fingers about for four or five minutes. (Salons sometimes put marbles or pebbles into their bowls for you to play with – like worry beads.) This exercises and relaxes your fingers and softens the cuticles at the same time.

An old-fashioned metal file is too harsh, and may actually rip your nails. (If your nails are long, and you have decided to shorten them, it is better to cut them with nail scissors or clippers, and then go on to an emery board.)

With the rough side of the emery, file each nail, working first from one side towards the centre, and then from the other side. Stroke after stroke, always in the same direction – from the sides in. Don't saw vigorously back and forth;

Dry your hands. Wrap the *blunt* end of an orange stick (the sharp end is only for cleaning under the tips) with cotton wool; dip it in the water and then gently – ever so gently – push back all your cuticles. Then do them all a second time.

You must never dig or prod at the cuticles. Although you can't see it, there is about a quarter of an inch of tender flesh at the base of each nail – the 'nail bed'. Move the tip of any nail up and down, and you will see this little area jiggle. It is the only part of your nail which is alive. The rest is dead. If you injure this living section, it will leave white spots and/or ridges on the nail when it grows out.

When the nail-bed is severely and permanently damaged (say, it has been caught in a car door or a drawer) its fingernail will be bumpy forever. There are other causes for ridged nails – rheumatism or arthritis, for instance. Sometimes they run in a family. Nothing you can do to avoid them in cases like that. But, for heaven's sake, don't bring them on yourself.

Rinse your hands again, and when you dry them, give every cuticle still one more little push with the towel. The soft/rough texture of the towelling is great for them. Do this, by the way, not only when you manicure, but every time you wash your hands.

If you have an extra ten minutes, follow with a hand massage (see p. 124). If you don't, promise yourself that you'll do it tomorrow, and splodge on some hand cream now. Work it well into your fingers and all over your hands.

Base coat/polish/top coat You have reached the polish stage. Dip a pad of cotton wool, this time into *soapy* water, and wipe over the surface of each nail to get rid of any oiliness left either from the remover or the creams. If you don't do this your polish won't adhere.

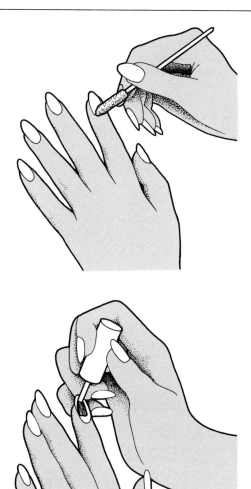

You start with a base coat. Always. This will be either colourless or a pale, pale pink. It does you a great many favours. It makes the polish stay on better. It prevents the surface of the nail from becoming discoloured, which it could do if you use dark shades of polish. Since most base coats now include strengtheners – synthetic fibres or ceramic substances – it will protect your nails from chipping should you bang them.

If you have a slightly cracked nail, there are mending products – quick-drying colourless glues – which come in small plastic phials, and which you apply before your base. A droplet will seal a small crack invisibly – rather like a china repair. (Don't bother to try if the crack is long and deep. In that case, you need a false nail.)

To apply the base, lay one hand down comfortably on your flat surface. Spread your fingers. Dip the brush into the bottle, and paint three strokes very thinly on each nail. Thin coats of any nail product look better and last better than thick ones. The first stroke goes from the centre of the cuticle to the tip; the other two go on each side, also from the cuticle upwards. Do all three in rapid succession so that the edges blend.

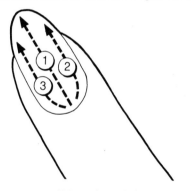

(Almost no nail is so broad that three strokes won't cover it.)

Don't worry too much about left-hand/right-hand favouritism. At first, the hand you use most regularly will paint more efficiently than the other. But it's a wonderful thing how applying nail varnish brings out the ambidexterity in all of us.

Let the base coat dry thoroughly. (All varnishes take slightly longer in a hot or damp climate.) Touch-test it with the tip of a finger. There should be no tackiness at all. When it is dry, you are ready for your colour.

Nail-colour, like make-up, should complement what you wear. Clashing colours look diabolical. Bright red is marvellous with black, grey or navy, but can be hideous with certain shades of purple. Deep reds and browns are always popular, but if they don't suit your wardrobe or your hands, disdain them. When in doubt, stay neutral with delicate coral or pink, which seem almost an extension of your natural skin tone.

The colour you choose can help your hands enormously – or call attention to their faults. With hands you wish you could hide away, it's a mistake to wear anything vivid. 'Look at me!' your nails will shriek. If bad circulation has made your hands purpley or blue, avoid the mauve ranges. If your nails are ridged, then frosted or iridescent polishes will only make the ridges more conspicuous.

The way you apply your polish can even help the shape of your nails. If yours are broad and squat, use a single stroke of colour down the centre, and leave the sides unpainted. This creates a convincing optical illusion of slimness, especially in a soft evening light.

And remember what I said about allergies. Should you have the slightest reason to believe that your varnish is in any way troubling your skin, try a different kind (non-frosted, for instance) or a different brand. If need be, give up varnish entirely. Better a clear complexion than dazzling nails.

Apply your polish very thinly, as you did your base. Three strokes per nail, from the cuticle upwards. Adequate drying time. But now you want a second coat. You can get away with only one, with a pale colour. You always need at least two with a dark shade.

You might want to go on to still another product, a 'top coat'. This is not essential, but it does add a strong, batter-resistant finish, and a nice flash of extra sheen.

If you get impatient while you're waiting for any layer to dry, or if the phone suddenly rings, give your nails a quick squirt of spray-dry. The polish underneath will still be damp, but the surface will have hardened enough to protect it from smudging. Many women finish with spray-dry whether they're rushed or not, both to get that extra surface-protection, and because most sprays contain cuticle conditioner.

How can you escape all that sitting and waiting? Why not put your base on in the morning, two layers of polish in the afternoon, and the top coat in the evening?

Your polish, if carefully applied, will look fine for about three days. By then, the tip-edges begin to wear slightly, and a sliver of white may show at the cuticle. Give them another layer of colour. Two or three days after that, apply still another layer.

But *not* if the polish has chipped. Once that has started, you must remove it completely. Whatever you do, don't peel it off. Not only does it look unsightly, but it takes the surface of the nail off with it.

New polish from old New polish is always easier to apply than polish that has gone a bit stale. Once the bottle has been opened and re-opened several times, it tends to get gummy. You can restore it to its proper consistency with varnish thinner, or solvent, as it is sometimes called. Some manufacturers supply a little plastic tube with which you can siphon up a drop or two, and then trickle it into the polish.

If your brand doesn't come with a tube, stand an orange stick in the polish and pour a miniscule stream of thinner out of its bottle and down the side of the stick. The stick will guide it safely home.

You may at some time buy a polish that you find too runny. Don't throw it away. You can, with the brush, dribble a few drops into polish that has gone tacky, thus making one good thing out of two bad ones.

You don't like colour? Then don't use it. Many women apply only a base coat, which protects their nails and gives them a soft sheen.

Or – there is now a big return to the nail buffer. I found a beauty in a junk shop, a charming Edwardian one with an ebony top and a soft white chamois base. But you can buy plastic-topped ones in most department stores and chemist shops.

You polish with a powder – a pink, powdery dust somewhat like jeweller's rouge. Put a little in the palm of your hand, pick it up with the buffer, burnish your nails briskly, one stroke at a time, and in one direction only. Rubbing the buffer back and forth works up friction, and will make your fingers uncomfortably warm. Buffing produces a lovely pink glow. Not only that, it tones up the circulation, stimulates the nails and strengthens them.

With either of these non-colour routines, give your nails a soigné finish by dampening a nail-whitening pencil and coating the inside of each tip.

False nails

These can be life-savers. They look so good that no one need ever know that they were not God-given. I always make a point of wearing at least two or three, whenever I give a demonstration. That proves two things: how convincingly real they appear, and how easy it is to work when you're wearing them.

They are the only solution for women who can't grow their own, for those whose professions prevent them from doing so, for nail-breakers and for nail-biters. Especially the last. You suddenly have a marvellous revelation. 'My hands can look fantastic!' The next thing you know, you will be growing yours. I speak from experience. I had been a nail-biter for years, and I was so encouraged the first time I wore false ones that I gave up the stupid habit on the spot.

False nails are actually helpful to problem nails. The glue provides a protective bubbly layer under which the real nail thrives healthily.

If you have never worn them before, allow yourself plenty of time to put them on – up to an hour. They take a bit of doing. And to begin with, apply them the day before The Day, so that you get used to the way they feel.

Wear either a complete set, or one or two – whatever number you need to match bitten or broken nails to an otherwise-handsome set. Manufacturers package false nails in different lengths and different widths, and there are always more than ten to a packet – at least fourteen or sixteen. You pick them to suit your needs.

One company gives you a double-sided sticky tape, so that you can line up the ones you select in sequence. But you can do this for yourself with sticky tape. Decide which you want by fitting them over the real ones.

The cuticle ends of false nails are always slightly rough, so the first thing to do is smooth them with an emery board. You can also shorten them with your emery. They must never be more than one-third longer than your own. If they project further than that, they simply won't stay on. Anyhow, if your own are very short, it is ludicrous to try to wear extremely long ones. You won't be able to cope. People with long nails use their fingers quite differently. If you're not accustomed to them, you could find yourself embarrassingly ham-handed.

When you try them on, make sure they fit snugly. Sometimes they don't curve quite enough. In that case, hold them under running *warm* water (not hot; high temperatures will melt them), then press them in lightly at the sides until they are perfectly rounded.

Your own nails must be absolutely clean. No polish. Nothing oily. You begin, however, with the false nails. Put a tiny smear of the glue that comes with the kit on the inside of the false nail. Start from the base, and go *no more* than two-thirds of the way up. Don't touch them for at least *thirty minutes*. Rush this, and you'll be in trouble. You can leave them overnight. You can, if you like, leave them for as long as two days.

When sticking-down time comes, apply the glue to your own nails. This you must leave for at least *ten minutes*. It doesn't feel gluey – only slightly gummy, like a self-sealing envelope. Don't touch the glue if you can avoid it. But you're not entirely crippled. You can, with care, use your hands. You could make yourself a cup of coffee, so long as you don't wet the glue. When the glue is dry, you will see those tiny bubbles that I mentioned, beneath the surface.

'Care' and 'precision' – those are the words for the application itself. The moment the two glue-covered surfaces come into contact, they adhere. So you must position them accurately.

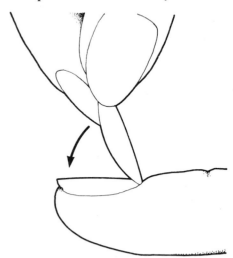

Hold the false nail up straight, with the cuticle touching and vertical to your own. Make certain that the false and the real are precisely aligned. Then let the false one drop into position. Press the two together for a minute or two, and you're in business. Varnish the false ones exactly as you varnish your own.

They are at their best for about a week. By then, your own nails, growing underneath, will begin to show at the cuticle end. When they reach that stage, the false ones tend to loosen. Whether they do or not, you should remove them. Your nail kit will contain a small capsule of remover. Read the instructions, pierce the capsule and apply. It takes only a couple of minutes. Then clean the glue off the nails and put them back in their box. You can re-use them indefinitely.

As you can see, I am all in favour of do-it-yourself false nails. But I am totally opposed to the kind that are phoney additions to your own. Salons do these, building them up with a heavy sort of ceramic stuff. When they apply this, the fumes are absolutely sickening. The surface of your own nails must be filed down before it will adhere. This weakens them, and it may take months before they recover. And the entire uncomfortable process has to be repeated regularly, to keep pace with the growth of your own. Models sometimes have to go through all this kerfuffle because their livelihood depends upon it. For the rest of us, it is extravagant, time-consuming and utterly silly.

Hand massage

Hand massage, like body massage, tones the circulation and loosens the joints. It also softens and smooths the skin, and keeps the fingers supple. Give your hands a thorough going-over every couple of weeks. But you should keep at it all the time by doing one bit or another of the routines I am about to describe every time you put cream on your hands.

Slather cream (either hand, or face-nourishing) onto the back of the hand you are going to massage, and hold it horizontally in front of you. Grasp it from above with the other hand, thumb on one side, and the four fingers on the other. The thumb does the hard work, but the fingers keep moving along with it in rhythm all the time, over the top and sides of the hand.

Starting high above the knuckles, at the sinews on the back of the hand, firmly work the thumb in a circular movement *down* the *bone joints* of the first finger. Then work the thumb *up* the same finger, this time *between* the bones and sinews. Up and down several times, always finishing with the same circular thumb movement over the back of the hand. Repeat, on all four fingers in turn. Massage the thumb itself with the thumb and first finger of the other hand. Move up and massage round the wrist. If you feel like it, work on up the arm, and give your elbow a good rub-over. Switch hands, and do the same all over again.

Next, open the fingers of one hand wide, and with the thumb and first finger of the other, pull hard on each finger in turn, two or three times for each. Change hands.

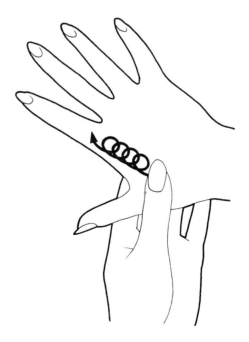

By now, you will probably need another dose of cream. Give yourself a generous dollop, and spread the fingers of both hands wide. With your palms together, interweave the fingers. Wiggle them back and forth, criss-crossing them strongly over each other. Continue for as long as you like – a minute or so, at least. Repeat – this time with your hands back to back.

Another exercise: let your fingers relax completely, and shake your hands back and forth as rapidly as you can. So fast that your hands become a blurred vision. Keep it up until you can feel the tingle. Splendid for the circulation, and for easing tiredness. Do this wherever and whenever you can.

A less energetic one: overlap your palms, and push the heel of one over and slightly above the other in a series of broad circular movements. Alternate the palm positions, and repeat. End by smoothing the fingers of both hands in the classic 'hand-wringing' motion of tragedy.

To finish: hold one hand out, letting the fingers fall free and relaxed. With the thumb and first finger of the other hand, take each finger in turn by its tip and rotate it four or five times. Do the same to the other. Keeps them supple.

Hand treatments

After you have finished your massage, fix yourself a hot-water bottle, and wrap it in a towel. Rub olive oil (or coconut, or almond oil) into your hands, and then put both hands into clean plastic bags. The bags will cling. Don't worry. They are there (a) so that if you have to do something like answer the phone, you can, (b) to intensify the effectiveness of the treatment, and (c) to keep the towel from getting oily. Put the water bottle on your lap, tuck your hands in under the flap where the towel ends, and sit there listening to dreamy music. This is wonderfully nourishing, and particularly good for you if you have been foolish enough to go out in the cold without gloves, and let your hands get chapped or sore or dry.

Should you have been even more ridiculous, and managed to get grime embedded in your hands by, say, gardening without gloves, try this: mix one tablespoonful of granulated white sugar or gritty brown sugar; one tablespoonful of honey; the juice of half a lemon, and a drop of olive oil. Plaster the mixture all over your hands, and rub it in gently for about five minutes. Then proceed as above with the plastic bags, taking your time over it. Enriching, softening and bleaching.

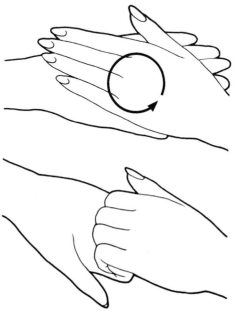

Feet

Everything I have said about hands goes for feet, too. For their sake and yours, they should be massaged and pedicured regularly. The procedures are almost identical to those for hand-care. But feet need one thing more: absolute comfort. If they're miserable, you're miserable – and it shows on your face.

Pedicure

The general principles are the same as for a manicure, with a few small exceptions. For a pedicure, you start on the soles and the backs of the heels, rubbing away any accumulation of dry skin. Left to build up, this can cause anguish, so you should do a rub-over (the bath is the best place) at least twice a week. But pedicure time is a good time to be extra thorough.

Use a pumice stone dampened in water, or take your choice of a number of gadgets which are sold by chemists and by foot-care specialists. Some are rather like rough, broad files; some, a little like graters; some, like ossified blocks of shredded wheat. There are also creamy liquids which you massage on. You roll them off, and the excess skin rolls off with them.

Because your toe-nails are tougher than your finger-nails, it is easier to cut or clip them to the right length than to file them with an emery board. You should, however, smooth them afterwards with the fine side of the emery. Always cut straight across the tops. Never cut diagonally at the sides; that is an open invitation to ingrown nails.

Treat the cuticles exactly as you do the cuticles on your hands.

When it comes to applying your polish, there is another slight difference. Since your toes don't spread naturally as your fingers do, you must keep them separated while the polish dries. Do this either with small pads of cotton wool between the toes, or with neat little devices made of foam rubber, which come in sets – wedges attached together, one for each foot.

Always finish – after a pedicure, a massage or a bath – with a dusting of talcum powder between the toes, to get rid of any moisture.

Foot massage

This is identical to hand massage – the same motions – and you're far better off because you can massage with both hands at the same time on each foot. Use hand cream, foot cream or body lotion. Cross one leg over the other or prop both feet up in front of you on a stool, whichever you find more comfortable. Work thoroughly round your toes, heels and ankles, and while you're at it, massage the cream on up your legs.

Corns, bunions, callouses and other curses

These happen only to feet which have been neglected or mistreated. The cause, more often than not, is ill-fitting shoes. If you have inflicted a corn or a callous upon yourself, tread warily with your treatment. *Never, never* take a razor blade to your feet. Use products made by specialists: pads to ease the pain and removers designed for the purpose.

Should your problem be feet that, well, aren't exactly as fragrant as the rose, be scrupulous about washing them daily and about a daily change of hosiery. (We all should be, of course, under any circumstances.) Never trap your feet in the same pair of boots or shoes for an entire day. (See Shoes, opposite.) This makes them uncomfortably hot, they perspire and – need I go on?

Counteract the discomfort caused by the heat by dunking your feet in tepid water, or by using a cooling foot-spray. (You don't have to bare your feet; the sprays are effective *through* nylon, and you can buy them handbag-sized to carry with you.) Fight the odour with deodorizing talcs or sprays, both between the toes and in your shoes; and by inserting into your shoes odour-absorbent inner soles with charcoal bases.

Imprisoning your feet can whiten them and cause nasty soft patches between the toes. They go mouldy, like damp walls. Next thing you know, you have a fungal infection.

'Athlete's foot' is the phrase that covers a lot of problems, from scaly patches to itchy, oozing sores between the toes. In the first instance, consult your chemist. There are numerous products (powder, unguent and liquid) which should deal expeditiously with mild cases. Serious cases call for the advice of a chiropodist, who may pass you on to a dermatologist.

With any persistent or painful condition, it is wise to put your feet into the safe hands of a chiropodist. He knows how to deal with your blights. You don't. More important, he will advise you on how to avoid contracting them again.

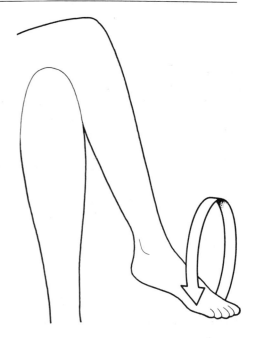

Foot exercise

Good for your arches, your ankles and for keeping your feet supple.

Cross your legs, point the toes of the top foot and perform a large circular movement with the entire foot. Repeat four or five times, and switch to the other foot.

Sit with both feet extended and slightly raised, and wiggle them round.

Sit with an empty milk bottle or coke bottle on the floor in front of you. Grasp it first with the toes of one foot, then with the toes of the other, rolling it back and forth six or seven times with each.

Put two or three marbles on the floor, and, from either a standing or a sitting position, lift them a few times, first with the toes of one foot, then with those of the other.

One of the best exercises of all is walking barefoot. Your feet love being unrestricted.

Shoes

This is a subject about which I get a bit fanatical. I cannot say enough about the havoc shoes can create. They must fit. The length, the width and the shape of the instep must all be precisely suited to your feet. It is better to buy a shoe a fraction too large, and to wear it with an inner sole, than to torture your feet by cramming them into a shoe a fraction too small.

Varying your heel-height is another excellent way to exercise your feet. It is even more necessary for your calves and thighs, which can get muscle-bound without the stretching that differing heel-heights provide. This is essential for women who work on their feet all day. I know. I do. And I always carry a change of shoes with me.

A medium heel is the most comfortable for working and walking. But do change about, as I said. Don't despair, however, if you cannot wear high heels. Some women can, as to the manner born, walking gracefully, elegantly. If they make you totter, or make you carry your entire body awkwardly (or make you taller than any man you know), then forget them. The world is full of pretty shoes with low or medium heels.

No matter what, buy the best shoes and boots that you can possibly afford. This is no extravagance. The uppers should always be leather. The soles, however, can quite safely be man-made. They wear well, and they do no harm to your feet.

But man-made uppers are catastrophic. They don't allow your feet to breathe. They don't move with them. They are constricting. They get over-hot and make your feet perspire, thus bringing on the curses I have mentioned above.

Two pairs of top-quality shoes in styles that don't date are a better buy than four pairs of sham-fashionable cheaper ones. Alternate the wearings; polish them; preserve their shape with trees; have them heeled when necessary, and they will serve you for years. The better you care for your footwear, the better they will care for your feet.

11. Excess hair and other nuisances

Excess hair

Hair is either gorgeous or a nuisance, depending on where it grows. Of course you want to encourage the first, and eliminate the second. There are five ways to do this: electrolysis; waxing; shaving; tweezing, or with depilatories.

Of them all, only *electrolysis* is permanent – or, to be strictly accurate, almost permanent. It must be done professionally. It is quite costly, it can be slightly painful and it may leave your skin feeling tender for about an hour.

A fine needle is inserted into the hair follicle, and an electric charge is passed through it, which deadens the root, after which the hair can be tweezed out easily. Strong, heavy hairs may need to be 'electrocuted' several times before they can be removed. There is a recent development, not yet in wide use, which speeds up the process and is less uncomfortable. This involves an electrified tweezer which kills the root and pulls out the hair simultaneously.

Hairs removed by electrolysis seldom grow back in the same place. New hairs, however, may shoot up very close to the old ones, and so the process might have to be repeated, perhaps as often as every six months.

The growth of hair and the frequency of its recurrence can be affected by the state of your health and by any medication you may be taking. The electrolysis operator should always ask what pills, if any, you are on, including the Pill, which changes the hormone balance. Thus she knows whether she is dealing with a natural or a medically-induced condition, and what reactions to expect.

Before you undertake electrolysis, verify that you are being treated by a reputable clinic or a top-quality beauty salon.

Waxing, which pulls the hair out from deep below the skin, is also slightly painful. But it is very efficient. It will last for up to six weeks with fine blonde hair, and about three, with coarse dark hair. The better the operator, the less twinge you will feel, and the more often you have it done, the less painful it becomes. It is always a bit more uncomfortable to do it yourself than to have it done in a salon. Once you have seen how it works, however, you can safely tackle it on your own.

Wax – either hot or cold – is applied to your skin. When it is pulled off, the excess hair is pulled out with it. It is like eyebrow plucking on a large scale.

Depilatories (cream, lotion or aerosol) are extremely easy to use. Simply rub them on and, after the prescribed number of minutes, wash them off and the hair washes off with them. Most depilatory manufacturers advise you always to test a tiny area first, and not to apply talcum powder or body lotions immediately afterwards.

Shaving and *tweezing* explain themselves.

Some techniques are more practical for certain problems than for others. Let us consider the hairy areas one at a time.

Eyebrows

You have already seen the diagram in the section on eye make-up. Study it again now, because it is when you trim your brows that you determine how effectively they frame your eyes. What you do with your make-up dramatizes the shape you have created.

The best possible relationship between the brow and the eye has been defined according to a formula which works for almost everyone. It works because, no matter how you may feel about either your eyes or your nose, they are by nature set in good balance with each other. Fashions change, of course, from time to time. There may be a sudden whim to bring brows closer together, or perhaps to flatten and lengthen the shape.

But in general, if you follow the principles in this diagram to achieve a broad, sweeping arch, you will like the way you look.

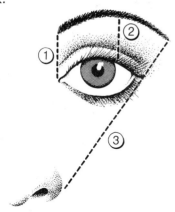

curve. Determine this point by holding the handle of a make-up brush against your face.

The outline should sweep upward gradually, broadening slightly as it rises, and slimming again as it moves downward. Avoid either an absolute semi-circle or a sharp angle at the top; both make you look shocked and surprised.

Women with heavy, unruly brows take it for granted that they must trim them. So also should women whose brows are fair and thin. We all have stray hairs above and below the arch; even if you can't see them (some blondes tweeze by touch), you must get rid of them so that you can put your eye make-up on smoothly.

Wherever possible, follow your own natural line, making adjustments as needed to shape each brow individually, and to make the two match. You are more likely to have to trim at the inner rather than at the outer ends. If your brows don't grow far enough at either extremity, cheat a bit with a pencil, as I said in Chapter 7.

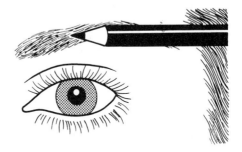

1. The eyebrow starts immediately above the inner corner of the eye.

2. The highest point of the brow, ideally, is directly above the outer edge of the iris. It should never be further in than the centre of the pupil.

3. The brow ends where a line extending from the corner of the nose meets the line of the brow on its downward

No matter how heavy your brows, don't be tempted either to shave them or to have them removed by electrolysis. The first will make them grow back in an ugly, protuberant stubble, not necessarily in the right place, and stronger than they were before. The second will remove them so completely that, should you change your mind and want to re-grow hairs where once they flourished, you will be unable to do so. For a tremendously heavy growth over the nose or, as occasionally happens, on the lids, waxing is very efficient.

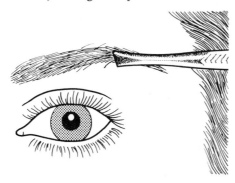

Most women find tweezing the easiest and wisest procedure. Tweezers come in assorted shapes and sizes, some with square ends, some pointed. I like small, neat pointed ones, but you may prefer something a little broader. Invest in a good pair with plenty of springiness. They should grip the hair firmly and not pinch the skin. Try them, by plucking a hair or two from the back of your hand before you buy them. If they are sealed in a packet and you are forbidden to try them, leave them in the shop. They are probably too cheap anyway to be any good (it is the shoddy ones usually that come sealed).

If you are doing the entire job all at once, especially for the first time, your flesh could go pink and feel slightly tender. A wipe-over with skin tonic on cotton wool will cool it. A consoling thought: once you have trimmed your brows well, you need never go through the whole business again.

Check them daily and, before you apply your foundation, pull out the odd straggler or two. About once a month (or even every other month, if your brows don't grow quickly), go over them more carefully to make certain they are keeping the line you have established. By then, perhaps, you might want to vary the line slightly.

Trim your brows in a good, clear light – daylight is better than artificial – and if your eyesight is not excellent, use a magnifying mirror. The best time to trim them is immediately after you have cleansed and toned your face, when your skin is supple. Apply moisturizer everywhere *except* your brows, so that it soaks into the rest of your face while you trim. If you put moisturizer on the brows themselves, it makes the hairs slippery and the tweezers won't grip.

Some women find that plucking is torment, even after cleansing and toning. If you are one, try doing it in your bath, when the warmth has opened your pores and made it comparatively easy for the hairs to slip out.

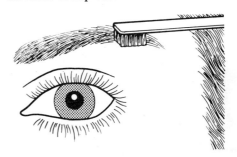

Brush through your brows with your stiff brush (eyebrow or clean old mascara brush), to groom them and to determine the line. Remove the hairs one by one. It is painful to yank them out in clumps, and it will produce a ragged outline.

Never trim your brows to a pencil-line thinness or to a hard, sharp edge. Never trim from the top, except for the odd hair or two that sprouts above the arch. The shaping should always be done from below, to give yourself the widest possible space from lid to socket to brow. (I have met only a few women whose socket area is so generous that they dare trim anything off the top.)

You may, if one brow is markedly lower than the other, and *if you use the utmost caution*, balance them by taking a few hairs from below the arch on one, and a few from above on the other.

Start with the stray hairs that grow furthest down, closest to the lid. Take a bit from each brow alternately, to keep them even. Move up to the next level, working horizontally all the way across. When you reach the bottom of the brow, go very gingerly, so that you establish a smooth line. Once the shape is settled, tweeze out any excess hairs above the nose and at the far ends.

You can thin dark and heavy eyebrows by pulling out a few hairs every so often along the main body of the arch, like weeding in a garden.

Should you encounter any hairs that are determined to resist you, don't battle with them. Don't try to excavate them. You could tear the surface of the skin. Better to let them have their way today and try again – perhaps in your bath – tomorrow.

Facial hair

Under no circumstances ever use a razor on your face. This is for men only. The easiest way to remove a light, fluffy growth is with a cream depilatory. Be certain that the packet specifies 'for use on face'. Remember, a tiny test-patch first. Then wait a full twenty-four hours to be sure you have no unpleasant reaction – itchiness or irritation – before you use it on the entire area. You may react badly to one brand but find another perfectly acceptable. Careful experimentation is the only answer. Be watchful, too, for any warnings about how long to wait before applying make-up.

Waxing is also safe for facial hair, and longer-lasting, of course, than cream removers.

A slight fuzz on the upper lip can be bleached – but never with a hair bleach, which is much too strong. There are many good facial bleaches available which will lighten the hairs almost to invisibility and, if used every couple of weeks, will eventually cause them to break off.

A real moustache or a heavy growth around the chin almost invariably needs electrolysis. From menopause onwards, such facial hairs tend to luxuriate distressingly. If they come up one or two at a time, you can keep them at bay with your tweezers. This has its drawbacks, however. Pulling them out makes them grow back stronger, and if they gradually increase in number to the point where you want them professionally removed, they will resist the operator and probably require several treatments.

Legs and underarms

Some women prefer never to touch the hair on their legs or under their arms. They like to be 'natural'. In Latin countries, I am told, men find this very sexy. Far be it from me to interfere with anyone's personal inclinations. There is, however, one proviso. If you don't remove the hair from under your arms, you must be extra fastidious about perspiration odours. This is not easy, because deodorants are not only difficult to apply to hairy skin, but are less effective than on smooth skin. (See p. 133.)

Legs covered with fine, blonde hair can glint quite attractively in the sunshine. Long, dark hair always looks unpleasant. It is possible to bleach a fairly thin growth. A thick growth really should be removed.

Depilatories are by far the easiest for taking the hair off your legs. The thicker the hair, of course, the longer it takes to dissolve. But it is worth the wait. Your legs will look good for about ten days, and when the hair grows back it will be soft. For a heavy growth, waxing is more sensible and more enduring.

Many women are devoted to the razor, chiefly because it is quick and convenient. If you are, then face the fact that you must keep at it constantly – at least twice a week – to keep fighting that unpleasant, raw-edged stubble.

If you insist upon shaving, invest in a good razor (electric, if you like, but it isn't necessary) or in a stock of those remarkable new cheap throwaways. Don't attack yourself with a blunt instrument. (And don't borrow your husband's razor. If I were a man, nothing would infuriate me more.)

For wet shaving, soap your legs – with shaving lather or soap – and follow with a dusting of talcum powder. With an electric shaver, powder before, to give yourself a dry surface.

As for shaving under your arms, 'Yes'. You do this so regularly – every few days – that the hairs never have time to grow back bristly. I find the bath most convenient. But never with an electric razor here: *electricity and water are a fatal combination*. A depilatory (test first, as always) is just as good. With either, never use a deodorant immediately afterwards. You should wait at least a couple of hours.

Body hair

Arms Unless the hair is very thick, bleaching is a good way out. Electrolysis is complicated, and to be considered only when the circumstance is desperate. A depilatory will deal with a moderate growth. If it is fairly heavy, waxing is a sensible solution, perhaps to be resorted to only in the summer, when your arms are exposed.

Stomach, breasts and shoulders There are seldom more than a few hairs, and they probably trouble you more than they do anyone else. The odd one here and there can always be tweezed out. With more concentrated clusters, both waxing and depilatories work. For heavy growths, electrolysis may be the answer. That depends upon how distressing you find the problem, and upon how much time and money you are prepared to spend.

Bikini line Pubic hairs have an exasperating way of straggling out when you move about on a beach. With only a few long strays, snip them off with scissors. For a denser bush, use a depilatory (the test-patch here is imperative) along the fringe of the V (not the entire pubic area) to leave a clean line above the bikini. Waxing is the most efficient of all. Have it done before your holiday; it will last about a month.

Some women depend on the razor for this too. To me, that is positively daft. This is the last place you want a rough, unpleasant stubble. And because the skin here is sensitive, shaving can make you break out in a rash or make you miserably sore.

Personal hygiene

Underarm

Our skin gives off moisture constantly, all over our bodies. It concentrates most heavily under the arms, where it is often embarrassing – damp patches that show on our clothes (and may ruin them) and off-putting odours.

You have your choice of two kinds of product: anti-perspirants, which stop the perspiration, diverting it to other parts of the body, where it is not accompanied by the distinctive (and unpleasant) underarm odour; and deodorants, which allow the perspiration to come through, but kill the smell. Fortunately, most women who used to believe that it was harmful in some undefined way to stop perspiration have now recognized that it is not. Consequently, most good underarm preparations now combine the needed double protection.

Deodorants come packaged as roll-on liquids, creamy sticks or in aerosols. I find the roll-ons the most satisfying. The sticks tend to leave a slight film, and the sprays may feel shockingly chilly. With sprays, there is also the possibility that I mentioned in Chapter 4 of an allergic reaction.

The skin under the arms can be exceedingly sensitive, and if you respond badly to deodorants, pick one that has no perfume. That is a good idea anyway. Why wear a fragrance in your arm-pits that is totally different from – and may even quarrel with – the cologne or perfume you put on later?

Several manufacturers now market deodorants designed for women who perspire unusually heavily. They cost a little more, but if that is your problem, they are worth it. Consult your chemist.

Let your deodorant dry thoroughly. You may feel a bit silly standing there waving your arms about in the air, but the better a deodorant dries, the better it works.

Some of those 'naturalist' women who refuse to remove the hair from under their arms also reject deodorants. They maintain that if they eat the right foods – a diet heavy on raw, green vegetables – or that if they take little green pills made of compressed chlorophyll or compressed parsley, they will kill the odour before it begins. Maybe . . . maybe . . . for a few. Frankly, I think they are taking a bit of a chance.

Vaginal

Different countries have different convictions. In the United States, no fastidious woman would live without her douche bag. On the continent, the *bidet* is the thing. I have even seen them in the public loos at Nice airport. In England, we depend upon neither. A daily bath or shower (one in the morning *and* one in the evening is better), with scrupulous washing, seems to keep us clean and fresh.

The private parts are so tender that you should use only the mildest soaps and never any preparations – liquid, impregnated pads, or whatever – which promise to deodorize. They can be harmful. Some women, indeed, dare not even use a perfumed soap, or wallow in a bubble bath. If you feel the slightest irritation, your safest bet is baby soap.

Halitosis

You should not suffer from it – not if you take care of your teeth, use a mouth-wash regularly and are reasonably healthy. Mouth odours often originate in the stomach, and a senseless crash-diet can bring them on with indecent haste.

Naturally, if you have eaten garlic or onions, the smell will linger. Use a mouth-wash when at home, a handbag-sized mouth spray when you're out.

Should halitosis be a persistent problem, consult your dentist or your doctor.

12. Fashion: the last word

So here you are in our last chapter – slim, streamlined thighs, flat stomach, straight back. Your hair, make-up, nails, feet – all are impeccable. Look at yourself in that merciless mirror. You are the kind of woman you wanted to be. Now for your clothes.

Let us think about that controversial and sometimes silly word, 'fashion'. What is fashion? An expert in one of our greatest stores said to me, 'Fashion is what sells.'

That means it's what *you* like, not what some self-appointed master-mind says you *should*. You buy it partly because it's 'in' this season, but, more importantly, because it looks good on you. Then you add to it your own individuality. Fashion is what you take off the rack. Style is the way you wear it.

Let me tell you a story. Not long ago, I was called in to make up eight models for a fashion show by a talented young designer. He had created a dream-like collection of pure silk clothes in subtle pastel shades – tight trousers, tabards, slinky long skirts, trailing scarves. He had assembled them by colour in complete outfits: soft olive green for one girl, apricot for another, powder blue for a third, and so on.

As they started to dress, one model said to her mate, 'That peach shirt would look smashing under this green tabard. Let me try it.' Before you knew it, the girls were swopping the colours around madly. Clouds of silk wafted back and forth across the dressing-room, and the designer stood there with his head swinging from one girl to another, as though he were watching a match at Wimbledon.

He didn't say a word, and I wondered whether he was going to blow his top. Suddenly he beamed: 'You girls are marvellous! You look wonderful! I can't thank you enough. You have made my show.'

He had given them glorious things to start with. The models, with their own innate flair and sense of style, had made them a hundred times more effective.

Good designers are not haughty dictators. They like to see women give their clothes a dash of originality. I was with a famous couturier when a client walked in. 'What do you think of this?' she asked him. She was wearing a beautiful burnt-umber and orange jacket that she had bought from him, with a pair of creamy beige trousers that she had picked up at a chain store for about one-tenth of the price of the jacket.

'Fantastic,' he said. 'The combination's great. I wish I had thought of it myself.'

Mixing and matching ingeniously, as far as I am concerned, is the secret of good taste and style. And women have never been so lucky. In any price range, we have an unbelievable choice. We can assemble imaginative outfits in good colours and in fabrics that wear well, wash and clean well, and serve us faithfully.

So why don't we all look terrific all the time? We could if we tried. It is largely a matter of planning ahead – not of scatter-buying, but of making an entire wardrobe work together, as an entity.

If all your good accessories are black or brown, it is mindless to bring home a navy-blue suit, no matter how stunning; it cries out for navy shoes and handbag – or grey ones, or red ones. You must build up an entire new set of accessories or ruin the suit by wearing it with the wrong things.

Certainly, you could get away with black shoes. But that's not the purpose of fashion, is it? Your clothes are supposed to make you feel good. It's a great ego-boost to know that everything you have on is exactly right. You are self-confident and poised.

You don't, however, have to be dressed in the very latest thing to feel as good as that. Every season produces a battery of new gimmicks, new looks. All are not for all of us. How could they be? The clever girl plays tricks with new ideas. She may twist her scarf this season's way, or wear a double belt, or a bow-tie or a frilly petticoat, not merely because they might be the last word, but because they're right for her. She takes what she likes, combines it with what she already has, and ignores the rest. She doesn't run out zombie-like and buy everything that everybody else is supposed to be wearing.

What I said about make-up and hair, I say even more forcefully about clothes. If a fashion doesn't suit you – because of your figure, your age or for any other reason, or if you just plain don't like it – make sure you don't let anyone bully you into buying it.

My own principle is to maintain a friendly relationship with fashion, without going overboard, always to buy the best that I can afford and to carry things over from year to year. You may prefer to own a lot of inexpensive clothes and to chuck them after every season. If so, you're not alone. I can't tell you how to spend your money. As for me, well, my husband says that I'm an awful hoarder. He's right. I can't bear to throw anything away.

The fact is that if you hold on to clothes long enough, they're bound to come back. I recently admired a suit an older woman was wearing. Absolutely on top of fashion: narrow skirt, little slits at the sides, broad shoulders. I asked her where she got it. She laughed: 'I had it made in 1950!'

There is a second point to that story. She had taken as much care of her figure as she had of her suit, and it still fitted perfectly!

'Best' and 'priciest' are not necessarily synonymous. I have known girls who have tied themselves into financial knots to buy clothes designed by Big Names. So devoted were they to the concept of *who* made it that they forgot almost entirely about how *they* looked in it. Some, I may say, looked dreadful. They might have been impressive if they could have worn everything inside out so we could read the labels. That sort of dress snobbishness is foolish conceit.

Even if your Name suit or coat flatters you enormously, the investment can become a burden. You feel you're forced to wear it and wear it, until it bores you and every one you know: 'Here she comes again, in her wearisome old What's-his-name!'

Such clothes eat up money that would do a lot more for your wardrobe if your budget were stretched to buy several good garments.

'Classic' – that is a word we have all had drummed into us. And a good sound word it is. I used it when I talked about shoes. I don't mind repeating it here.

In dress terms, I define it as simple and well cut, uncluttered, unfaddy, well made, and in plain colours that blend and tone with each other. A wardrobe composed of classic shirts, blouses, jackets, waistcoats, jerkins, tabards, sweaters, skirts and trousers is the most flexible and useful wardrobe a woman can have. Add to this the odd perky (inexpensive!) shirt and the odd silly-season (inexpensive!) trousers, plus the proper accessories – earrings, necklace, handbags, shoes, scarf – and you can hardly ever go wrong.

Buy a dress and you have – only a dress. Oh, yes, you can change the belt or switch buttons or wear a jacket over it, but it is still basically the same dress. Buy separates and you can match and mix endlessly. If, as I said, you remember to think of your wardrobe as an entity, you will have provided yourself with infinite variety at comparatively little cost.

The biggest mistake of all, unless you live high off the hog, dining out and dancing night after night, is to spend a great deal on an evening dress and then to see it hanging there for months on end, limp, wan and unloved. Much better to own a couple of good long skirts or a couple of pairs of dressy slacks, and a selection of blouses, tabards, tunics and frilly shirts. Or to buy an eye-catching evening jacket to go over an old long dress than to pay again for an entirely new one.

Whenever you shop, know what you intend to buy. Define your colour range – say, *anything* that will be right with your new brown coat, from beige to coral to rust to a toning brown. Or the *one* specific colour that you must have – pale pink, say, for a blouse to wear with deep pink slacks. If you want to tone with or match a garment you already own, take it along with you. It is hard to carry an exact shade in your memory – much easier to carry the garment itself in a bag.

Once you have made up your mind, be unswerving. You will hate yourself and the thing you buy if you settle for an almost-but-not-quite-right.

Having said all that so firmly, may I now make an exception?

Shopping trips can disclose unexpected wonders. Mine often do. If I suddenly come on something that is perfect for me; if I can anticipate its useful-

ness; and (yes, I repeat) if it fits into my wardrobe, I will buy it. This is likely to turn out to be the very skirt or velvet top that will solve my problem when I am unexpectedly invited to dinner a week from tonight.

A new garment, unworn for a little while, is like a good insurance policy. It saves you from a frantic, panic-buying rush when an unheralded invitation slips through your letter-box.

Which brings me to shopping at sales. I'm all in favour. It's a splendid way to collect better clothes than you could ordinarily afford – so long as you buy at a reliable store, and so long as you don't get carried away. The slashed price on the sales ticket should be your last, not your first criterion. What value a sexy pair of purple satin slacks marked 'Half Price' if you haven't a thing to wear with them – or any place to wear them to? Or a pair of thigh-high yellow boots that clash with everything you own?

Ask yourself, 'If I had had the money would I have bought it at its full price? Or is the enormous mark-down making me dizzily irresponsible?' If you are convinced that you would have had it in any case, you could be on to a winner.

Even then, hesitate. Is it practical? Is the colour too pale for everyday wear? Will it stay comparatively unwrinkled? Wash well? Pack well?

Is it comfortable? You've been exasperated in the past by sleeves too narrow, collars chokingly tight, waistbands that pinch or slacks that bind at the crotch. Don't cramp or trap yourself again.

Sales time or any other, do be certain that what you buy becomes you. Consider that constant nagging problem of skirt-length. Your skirt should stop at the line on your calf which flatters your leg the most – slightly lower down if your legs aren't exactly super, slightly higher up if they are. The length should also do as much as possible for your entire figure. A tall woman looks beautifully graceful in a longish skirt; in the same skirt a short, dumpy woman can appear to be walking on her knees.

Certain errors are so glaring that it seems almost superfluous to point them out. Yet – yet – how many short, stocky girls do you know who will insist upon broad horizontal stripes, huge checks or large prints, despite what their own eyes must (and their best friends do) tell them? And how many tall ones do we see in long, skinny dresses with long, skinny stripes?

The whole thing baffles me. The rules are so self-evident. A tall thin woman can do what she likes about big patterns and about boldly mixing colours – a bright red shirt with green slacks, or a yellow one with purple. Let a short, stout woman try the same, and she cuts herself in half at the middle, and becomes that much shorter and stouter.

Simple dark clothes, of course, are more slimming than fluffy, light-coloured ones. But why not compromise? A muted single colour can be remarkably becoming to a stoutish figure if the cut, the fit and the length are right. This is a better idea for a woman with a few pounds to lose than to hide incessantly under black, flowing tents. They conceal the problem. They do nothing, however, to urge you to correct it.

Some faults should undoubtedly be concealed. Arms, before the flab has been well and truly firmed, are more appealing covered than sleeveless. Colossal hips are less conspicuous in full skirts than crammed sausage-like into slim ones. Long giraffe necks benefit from soft, rolling high collars, and flat breasts from loose gathered blouses.

Assets, on the other hand, should be revealed. A good bust? Show it off! A fine figure? Then you're mad if you clutter up your waistline and hide all the rest of you away, no matter what's in fashion!

As for age, well, this one is more difficult. Of course, it is pathetic to see

right   wrong

women in their middle years flouncing about in short little dresses or in tight jeans that were cut only for teenagers. But there is no one terrible, calendar-designated year at which style-sense turns off. For that, let us all be grateful.

As a woman matures, her clothing inclinations tend to become more elegant. If she keeps her figure and makes up well, she can wear almost anything that takes her fancy. And, lucky older woman, she can do what most younger ones find a little difficult. She can be as highly individualized – even eccentric – as she pleases. She has been at it for years. She is certain of herself. If capes are her thing, or broad-brimmed hats, or fur muffs – and she knows she wears them with panache – she can shrug off anyone who tries to tell her that she's not in tune with the time.

Let us return to the all-together woman who knows how to juxtapose it

all – the newish skirt with the oldish blouse, and shoes of the correct heel-height with a handbag of the correct colour. Throughout this book I have spoken of her in terms of things you can see – her figure, skin, hair, make-up and so on.

She has one thing more which completes her total impact. And this one is invisible. Her perfume. Unseen, it creates a mood, an ambience.

I once found a beautiful silk scarf in a London shopping street. I stood waving it about for a quarter of an hour, hoping that whoever had dropped it would come back for it. No one did, and I took it home. That scarf fascinated me, not only because it was delicate and soft and prettily designed, but because of the fragrance that permeated it.

It was a delicate odour that clung for days, and every time I picked the scarf up I tried to envisage the invisible woman who had owned it. She was chic, of that I was certain. The scarf itself made that apparent. And she was elegant and tasteful. Her perfume told me so.

It is delightful when a lovely woman walks into a room if a lovely fragrance floats in with her. Some like to wear the same scent all the time, to make it a sort of personal trademark. Unmistakably, pleasingly theirs.

I like to vary my fragrances – lighter, slightly sharper in the summer, more sultry in the winter, and different from day to day.

Perfume must never be overpowering. A little goes a long way, and too much can be almost asphyxiating to others. The best, oil-based perfumes are too costly, anyway, to slosh on over-generously. But in the past few years, manufacturers have evolved scents made of synthetics which are quite as fragrant as the real thing and a great deal less expensive.

Buy them as perfumes, essences, colognes, toilet waters, or in sticks (ideal for travelling). Choose them because they please you, and the people who matter most to you.

If your skin is allergic to perfumes, spray them on your hair or clothes. But watch out for those that are oil-based: they will stain fabrics. If your skin can tolerate them, wear them on the pulse points, which helps diffuse them: the wrists; behind the ears; behind the knees; inside the elbows.

However you move, then, your perfume pulsates with you. As indeed it should. It is meant to be sensual. Nothing is more evocative. Nothing triggers off memories so strongly as a fragrance you associate with days or nights of happiness.

Perfume is frankly feminine. And femininity is what this book is all about.

Acknowledgements

During the time spent writing this book it was great to have the help and encouragement of so many good friends. I would especially like to thank Charlotte and Denis Plimmer, without whose help and enthusiasm the book might never have been written; Derek Morris, my hairdresser, who not only helped me with the book, but who has kept my hair under control as long as I can remember; Vince Loden, who took the photographs; Judy Dear, Annegret, Daisika and Dee, who modelled for them; David Blair for Daisika's hair; David Woodroffe, who drew the line illustrations; Maggie Patten for a superb typing job, done under great pressure; and finally I would like to thank everybody in the beauty and fashion world I have enjoyed working with for so many years.